PROPERTIES of MEMBRANES

Based on the Symposium — June 1961 — Sponsored
Jointly by the American Neurological Association and
the American Association of Neuropathologists, Inc.

PROPERTIES of MEMBRANES

and Diseases of the Nervous System

By

DONALD B. TOWER · SARAH A. LUSE · HARRY GRUNDFEST

With discussions by

ABEL LAJTHA · MURRAY B. BORNSTEIN · ICHIJI TASAKI

Foreword by MELVIN D. YAHR

SPRINGER PUBLISHING COMPANY, INC.

NEW YORK

Foreword

The American Neurological Association and the American Association of Neuropathologists have over the years devoted a portion of their annual scientific meetings to joint presentation of topics of mutual interest. By and large, these have concerned themselves with bringing together the latest clinical and pathological concepts of a specific disease entity. The 1961 program was a departure from this traditional format. It was selected in recognition of the expanded area of research made possible by the development of newer techniques and their application to the neurological sciences. The result has been a new body of data which, though still in an emergent stage, has had a profound effect on our concepts of the form and function of the nervous system.

Though it is becoming apparent that many of the membranes of the body have a number of features in common, including their macromolecular pattern, nowhere in the human organism are they more intimately related to function than in the nervous system. Not only do they act as selective barriers producing separate functional units, but they are also intimately related to the vital mechanisms of conduction, transmission and reception of nerve impulses. At long last our investigations are approaching the molecular or at least the macromolecular level of central nervous system function, so essential for an understanding of its role in normal as well as pathological conditions.

In bringing together the neurochemist, electronmicroscopist and neurophysiologist under a broadly headed topic, *Properties of Membranes and Diseases of the Nervous System,* it is hoped that some of these new horizons in neurology can be seen in their proper perspective. Each of the essayists has been given free rein in selecting those membranes which best exemplify the approach of his own discipline. No attempt has been made to seek common ground to explain a specific functional activity of nervous tissue but the interaction of each of these approaches becomes readily apparent to the reader. Though each may differ in defining the very meaning of "membrane," it is obvious that the chemist's concern about essential metabolites cannot be readily separated from the physiologist's involvement in the electrical excitability of the structure through which these substances must pass. Nor can either of these be fully appreciated except in terms of their morphological characteristics as seen in the electron microscope.

Though much of the material to be found in these pages concerns the nervous system in its normal state, the transition to the study of pathological conditions seems well within our reach.

MELVIN D. YAHR, M.D., *Editor*

List of Contributors

Murray B. Bornstein, M.D., Research Associate, The Mount Sinai Hospital; Director, Laboratory of Cellular Neurophysiology, The Mount Sinai Hospital, New York, New York

Harry Grundfest, Ph.D., Professor of Neurology, Columbia University College of Physicians and Surgeons, New York, New York

Abel Lajtha, Ph.D., Associate Research Scientist, New York State Research Institute for Neurochemistry and Drug Addiction; Assistant Professor of Biochemistry, Columbia University, New York, New York

Sarah A. Luse, M.D., Associate Professor, Departments of Anatomy and Pathology, Washington University, St. Louis, Missouri

Ichiji Tasaki, M.D., Laboratory of Neurobiology, National Institute of Mental Health, National Institutes of Health, Bethesda, Maryland

Donald B. Tower, M.D., Ph.D., Chief, Laboratory of Neurochemistry, National Institute of Neurological Diseases and Blindness, Bethesda, Maryland

Contents

Molecular Transport across Neural and Non-Neural Membranes

Donald B. Tower

Peculiarities in distribution of solutes between external fluids and cells have been recognized since Liebig (88) pointed out over a century ago that potassium was primarily an intracellular ion and sodium characteristically an extracellular ion. The apparent impermeability of many cell membranes to sugars, the main metabolic fuels for these cells, led to suggestions by Overton (104) among others that sugars were transferred into cells as lipid-soluble derivatives or complexes. Subsequently Van Slyke and Meyer (148) demonstrated that the free (non-protein) α-amino nitrogen (or amino acid) content of tissues was maintained at levels 5 to 10 times higher than that of blood. Such observations led Höber (57) to postulate devices in the cell membrane which could regulate the exchange of solutes, a concept which he termed "physiological permeability" in contrast to physical permeability.

These few examples emphasize the long history of the subject and indicate the acuteness of early investigators in anticipating much of what may now be discussed in more precise, albeit still incomplete, terms. The limitation of this paper to transport of molecules is purely a device of convenience since there is basically little distinction between "ions" and "molecules" in this context. Both groups share common characteristics in biological solution and in their modes of transfer across biological membranes. A number of amino acids, for example, are not generally discussed under ion transport but commonly exist in biological fluids as charged molecules or ions. Conversely, familiar inorganic ions usually exist in such fluids as hydrated complexes [$e.g.$, Na $(H_2O)_n^+$] and hence assume some of the properties of molecules.

For the nervous system relatively more attention has been devoted to ion fluxes and transport across the excitable, conducting membrane. Less

1

is known about the corresponding fluxes and transport of other solutes, carbohydrates, amino acids and the like, although obviously the latter are essential to neural cell metabolism which provides the requisite energy to support ion transport. There is, however, a very considerable literature on solute transport across other cell membranes, such as erythrocytes, skeletal muscle, intestinal mucosa, renal tubules and bacteria, and these can serve in many cases as analogies for transport mechanisms across neural membranes.

Consequently my approach to the subject has been a dual one. On the one hand, a brief summary of a number of basic principles which apply to solute transfer across membranes in general has been included to provide a framework within which subsequent discussions may be more intelligible. On the other hand, certain examples have been selected of how carbohydrates, amino acids and other compounds are transferred across non-neural membranes as indicative of the types of mechanisms characteristically encountered. With these as reference points, some examples of comparable transfers of solutes across neural membranes can be considered. No attempt has been made to include pathological aspects except in incidental examples since this would seem to represent a subject in itself and to be somewhat premature at our present stage of knowledge. As far as neural membranes are concerned, we appear to be on the threshold of rapidly expanding progress in the study of the subject. For this we are indebted to the prodigious labors of many diverse investigators in other fields upon whose experiences and techniques we can now fruitfully build.

Membranes and Compartments

Solutes and metabolites must traverse many membranes during their passage into or out of the plasma pool (Fig. 1). Major interchanges occur at the capillary membrane, the interstitial (extracellular) fluid, the cytoplasmic membrane, and the intracellular fluid. The solutes may be grouped into two major categories, *lipophilic* or readily soluble in lipids present in most membranes but with difficulty soluble in the aqueous fluid phases, and *hydrophilic* or aqueous soluble but for practical purposes insoluble in membrane lipids. Body fluids are geared primarily to dealing with hydrophilic solutes, so that the existence and passage of lipophilic substances in body fluids require special mechanisms, such as complexing with proteins (103), to permit their transport therein. By contrast, lipophilic substances readily penetrate lipoidal membranes usually by passive diffusion (35, 103), whereas hydrophilic solutes encounter barriers here which require special transport mechanisms for penetration through them. Some of these mechanisms are indicated schematically in Figure 1.

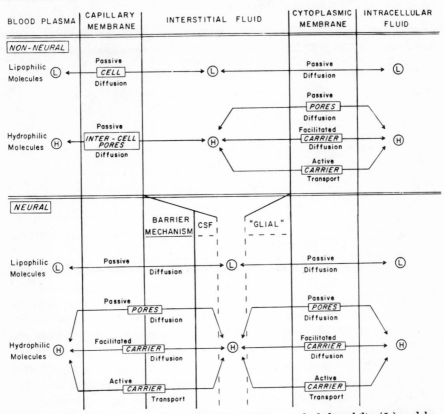

Fɪɢ. 1.   Schematic summary of the principal membranes which lipophilic (L) and hydrophilic (H) solutes must traverse in passage between blood and tissue cells in both non-neural and neural tissues. Major transport devices and processes are indicated. See text for discussion.

The situation in the central nervous system is similar with two exceptions. At or near the capillary membrane the blood-brain barrier is interposed as an additional membrane or membrane-like mechanism between blood and interstitial fluid and cells. In addition the central nervous system does not exhibit the simple interstitial fluid space found in most tissues, but a complex of at least three parts, the cerebrospinal fluid (CSF) external to the tissue mass, a true interstitial fluid space of relatively limited volume, and a fluid compartment apparently within certain glial cells (probably astrocytes) which is in relatively free communication, as far as water and small solutes are concerned, with the other two (29, 40, 91). For most hydrophilic substances of small molecular size (sugars, amino acids, inorganic ions) all three spaces appear to be freely accessible and in func-

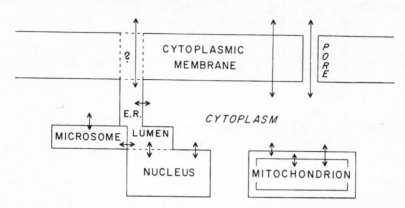

Fɪɢ. 2. Simplified scheme of the principal intracellular membranes found in most cells, indicating major intracellular compartments and potential sites for intracellular transport processes across the membranes separating these compartments. See text for discussion. (E.R.=endoplasmic reticulum.)

tional intercommunication. Despite the morphological complexities exemplified under electron microscopy, the three fluid subdivisions behave for practical purposes like the interstitial space of other tissues,* with the possible exception of some restriction on free interchange of solutes of relatively large molecular size (*e.g.,* inulin) across the "glial" compartment.

In addition to the principal membranes indicated in Figure 1, there are numerous membranes within cells which may require special processes for solute transfers across them. Some of these intracellular membranes common to many cells, including neurons, are schematically shown in Figure 2. Of relevance to the preceding discussion is the situation with respect to the lumina of the endoplasmic reticulum tubules. On both morphological (130) and functional (121, 151) grounds it has been suggested that some of these lumina may communicate at least intermittently with the cell exterior and hence their fluid content be functionally part of the extracellular space. The dimensions of these lumina are compatible with calculations that in-

* This statement is supported by biochemical measurements of chloride, sucrose and thiocyanate spaces comparable to those in other tissues (25, 109), by physiological data from impedence (146) and microelectrode (86, 87) studies which require a "functional" extracellular space, and by morphological evidence of fluids shifts in these spaces (29, 40, 91). The factor of artifact has not been excluded from electron micrographs showing apparently no visible extracellular space in brain, since fixation of such specimens is not without volume changes (H. M. Pappius, unpublished data) and since, under normal circumstances fluid spaces unbounded by enclosing membranes may not be well preserved in the absence of sufficient high molecular weight substances for fixation therein.

Table 1. COMPARTMENTATION

Level	Components
1. Organ	Vascular Extravascular (barrier mechanism)
2. Tissue	Extracellular (CSF; "glial") Cellular — neurons glia (3 types) endothelial
3. Cellular	Perikaryon Processes — dendrites axon synapse
4. Subcellular	Nucleus (nucleolus) Mitochondria (cristae; "fluid") Endoplasmic reticulum (membranes; microsomes) Other "particulate" components Cytoplasmic fluid

Reference: 151

dicate a layer of interstitial fluid of the usual ionic composition only 6 Å thick would be necessary to charge the cell membrane capacity to 90 mV. (161). The extension of some lumina to surround the cell nucleus has also been proposed (130). Thus, the membranes of the endoplasmic reticulum are probably as important for solute transfers within cells as the mitochondrial membranes which are recognized to be osmotically active and to exhibit differential permeabilities. In fact, it has recently been suggested that the endoplasmic reticulum membranes represent an important site for ion fluxes and transport in both muscle (121) and neuron (94, 162).

An important corollary to the existence of many extra- and intracellular membranes is the compartmentation of the various processes taking place in tissues and cells. It has long been appreciated (58) that metabolic functions within cells must be compartmented to permit synthetic, degradative and other activities to proceed simultaneously in an orderly fashion. Nowhere is this more obvious than in such a complex organ as the central nervous system (Table 1), as several recent discussions have emphasized (141, 151, 152). Obviously compartmentation also represents an important factor in the distribution of solutes across membranes. The exclusion of certain solutes from the central nervous system by the blood-brain barrier and the differential distribution of ions between interstitial and cellular compartments are familiar examples. Within neural cells the segregation of about one-third of the total cellular potassium within mitochondria (62)

Table 2. MECHANISMS OF TRANSFER OF MOLECULES
ACROSS MEMBRANES

1. Passive Diffusion
   (a) Bulk transfer
   (b) "Pore-restricted"

2. Facilitated (Mediated) Diffusion
   (a) Exchange diffusion

3. "Active" (Energy-Linked) Transport
   (a) Exchange diffusion

4. Pinocytosis and Phagocytosis

5. Specialized Mechanisms (e.g., viral invasion)

and the demonstration that systemically supplied C^{14}-glutamic acid mixes initially with only about 4% of the total cellular free pool (152) are additional examples. At the present time data are too fragmentary to permit a detailed consideration of compartmentation factors in transport processes, but it must be borne in mind that such factors apply in all but the simplest situations and that they may considerably complicate the ultimate interpretation of data now available for most tissues.*

General Principles of Solute Transfers

The majority of mechanisms utilized by biological systems for transfer of solutes across membranes are summarized in Table 2. If the more specialized mechanisms are excluded, the commoner mechanisms fall into two large groups, those that are passive and operate by diffusion, and those that require the mediation of a carrier or transporter. The general principles relevant to these two modes of transfer are indicated schematically in Figure 3.

Passive diffusion (Fig. 3, left) depends upon the permeability characteristics of the solute in question and upon the degree of concentration gradient for the solute across the membrane. Concentration gradients usually

---

* A recent study by Allfrey *et al.* (*Proc. Nat. Acad. Sci.*, 47: 907, 1961) on isolated calf thymus nuclei illustrates this point very well. The isolated cell nuclei exhibited uptake of amino acids which was sodium-dependent and had properties analogous to bacterial "permease" systems (discussed subsequently in the text), including active transport, exchange diffusion, stereospecificity, competition, etc. The authors place particular stress on the role of sodium (in contrast to the association of cytoplasmic transport processes with potassium) and suggest a close relationship of transport across nuclear membranes with extracellular fluid (cf. discussion in text of Fig. 2).

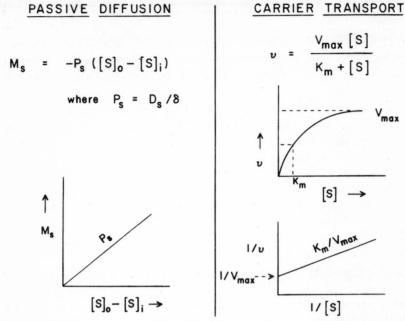

PASSIVE DIFFUSION

$$M_s = -P_s ([S]_o - [S]_i)$$

where $P_s = D_s / \delta$

CARRIER TRANSPORT

$$v = \frac{V_{max} [S]}{K_m + [S]}$$

FIG. 3. Basic mathematical principles describing the processes of passive diffusion (*left*) and carrier-mediated transport (*right*), as discussed in the text. *Abbreviations*: For *passive diffusion*: M_s—net unidirectional flux of solute (S). P_s—permeability coefficient of the solute derived from the diffusion coefficient (D_s) characteristic of the solute and the membrane thickness (δ). $[S]_o$ and $[S]_i$ represent concentrations of solute in external (o) and internal (i) fluid phases. For *carrier transport*: v—rate of transport of solute (S). V_{max}—maximal rate of transport. [S]—concentration of solute in the phase from which transport takes place. K_m—the equilibrium constant (analogous to the Michaelis-Menten constant) of dissociation of the carrier-solute complex.

arise as a result of hydrostatic or osmotic (electrochemical) differences across the membrane. In such a situation, as the concentration gradient is increased, there is a linear increase of solute net flux, normal to the gradient, across the membrane, as illustrated graphically and by the diffusion equation (30) shown in the figure.

By contrast, carrier transport has as its most characteristic feature the phenomenon of saturation, *i.e.*, as the concentration of the solute is increased on one side of the membrane, the rate of flux, normal to the concentration gradient, reaches a maximum (V_{max}) beyond which it will not go regardless of how much higher the gradient is pushed (Fig. 3, right upper graph). This phenomenon was quickly recognized to be closely analogous to saturation of an enzyme by its substrate, the kinetics and mathematical expressions for which were first propounded by Michaelis and Menten (95). The equation describing saturation kinetics (Fig. 3, top right) contains the Michaelis-Menten constant (K_m), which provides an inverse measure of the affinity of the enzyme (or carrier) for its substrate. Hence the smaller the K_m, the more readily combination of the two occurs and vice versa. When several substances compete for the same enzyme (or carrier) the respective K_m values for the various substances are indicative of their relative behaviors in the system. Since the simple plot of such a system is non-linear, various derivations have been introduced which yield a linear plot from which the maximal rate (V_{max}) and K_m values can readily be derived. A common type is the Lineweaver-Burke plot (89) illustrated by the lower right graph of Figure 3. The apparent correspondence between enzyme and carrier saturation kinetics does not necessarily imply that carrier-mediated transport processes are enzymatic in nature, but the analogy has proved most useful in studying transport phenomena (18, 156).

Water transfers.   Perhaps the most familiar example of passive diffusion is the transfer of water across membranes. In most biological systems it is generally agreed that water movement is purely passive (117, 118), as shown diagrammatically in Table 3. Assuming a membrane impermeable to solutes but permeable to water, the water will distribute in three phases, externally, within the membrane, and internally. If the concentration of solutes on the two sides is different, the osmotic differences created will cause water to flow across the membrane as depicted. This phenomenon is more understandable if the water is considered not as a solvent but as a concentration of molecules, which in this example form different mole fractions of the total contents (water + solute molecules) on the two sides of the membrane. Thus, the concentration gradient for water becomes apparent and diffusion in accordance with the principles already discussed (Fig. 3) can be appreciated.

Typical examples of water diffusion are included in Table 3. In the kidney the hydrostatic pressure of arterial blood produces filtration (or diffusion) of about 20% of the renal blood water (and solutes) across the glomerular membranes into the renal tubules per minute (72). Water transfers of this magnitude are usually considered to represent bulk flow in contrast to restricted flow through less porous membranes.

If an osmotic difference is created across a semi-permeable membrane, such as the toad skin, net water flow as measured by heavy water (D_2O) rises from zero at equi-osmolarity to an appreciable rate at osmotic differences of 1:10. Addition of antidiuretic hormone (ADH) increases the net diffusion flow 2- to 4-fold further, due to the effect of the hormone on the size of the membrane pores through which diffusion occurs, yet the hormone induces no effect in the absence of an osmotic difference across the membrane (3, 73).

Studies on the entry of heavy water (D_2O) into the central nervous system have demonstrated extremely rapid rates of diffusion in both dog and man (6, 133). Compared to the rate of entry of radioactive sodium (Na^{24}) into cisternal CSF, the entry of D_2O was at least 100 times faster but this rate was only 1/15 the rate of D_2O entry into brain tissue.

Membrane "pores." In view of the lipid nature of most membranes which water and hydrophilic solutes must traverse, the existence of water-filled "pores" or channels through which diffusion across the membrane can occur has been postulated (107, 127). In the toad skin study cited (Table 3), convincing evidence was presented by Andersen and Ussing (3)

Table 3. PASSIVE DIFFUSION OF WATER

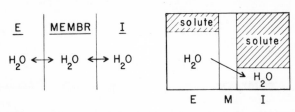

Tissue	Conditions	Observations		
		Plasma Flow		Filtration Rate
Human kidney	Hydrostatic pressure	655 ml./min.		127 ml./min.
		Net D_2O Flow Osmolarity Equal		($\mu l/cm^2/hr$) Osmolarity 1:10
Toad skin	Osmotic pressure			
	Control	0-3		20- 22
	+ ADH	0-2		50-104
		Half Equilibrium Time with Plasma		
		D_2O		Na^{24}
		Dog	Man	Man
Brain (Dog; Man)	Isotope exchange			
Cerebral cortex		12 sec.	–	–
Subcortical white		20 sec.	–	–
Cisternal CSF		3 min.	1.5 min.	370 min.
Ventricular CSF		8 min.	11 min.	82 min.
Lumbar CSF		7 min.	25 min.	550 min.

References: 3, 6, 72, 133

Table 4. MEMBRANE "PORES"

Membrane	Effective Pore Radius	Per cent of Total Surface Occupied by Pores
Capillary	30-45 Å	< 0.2
Toad skin	6-20 Å	–
Nerve	~ 2 Å	< 0.02

Ion or Molecule	Crystal Ionic Radius	Effective Hydrated Radius $[X(H_2O)_n^+]$
H_2O	–	~ 2 Å
Na^+	0.95 Å	3.4
K^+	1.3	2.2
Cl^-	1.8	2.2
Ca^{++}	0.65	5.9
Mg^{++}	1.0	4.5

References: 3, 107, 127

for restricted areas in the membrane through which water and solutes must diffuse. These investigators demonstrated the occurrence of "solvent drag," *i.e.*, the retardation of diffusion of solute molecules in the direction opposite to the direction of water diffusion, a phenomenon which requires some type of channelling of solvent and solute movements. From the degree of "solvent drag" the effective radius of such channels or pores could be calculated (Table 4). The effect of antidiuretic hormone in these experiments was interpreted as increasing the "effective" pore size (either actual increase of pore diameter or opening up additional pores) and thus facilitating or speeding diffusion. Comparable effects of this hormone on water reabsorption by kidney tubules (72) and on solute penetration across the blood-brain barrier (34) have been similarly interpreted.

A few data on membrane pore sizes and the fractions of total membrane surface occupied by pores are given in Table 4, together with comparable radii of some common inorganic ions. In capillary membranes the "cement" spaces between endothelial cells are thought to be the sites of water and hydrophilic solute diffusion (12, 107), and hence are relatively large compared to cellular membrane pores, presumably exemplified by nerve in Table 4. Gases and lipophilic solutes diffuse readily across the total extent of capillary membranes and probably also across the major extent of most cell membranes. Obviously few ions in the hydrated state and virtually none of the larger molecules like sugars and amino acids would readily diffuse through pores as small as those in nerve.

Table 5. OXYGEN TRANSPORT BY HEMOGLOBIN

LUNG ‖ BLOOD ‖ TISSUE

$$HHbO_2 \longrightarrow HHbO_2$$

$$O_2 \longrightarrow \uparrow \qquad \downarrow \longrightarrow O_2$$

HHb   HHb

$$CO_2 \longleftarrow \uparrow \qquad \downarrow \longleftarrow CO_2$$

$$HbCO_2 \longleftarrow HbCO_2$$

	Lung (pG mm Hg)	Tissue (pG mm Hg)	Tissue Delivery (% of Requirement)
Oxygen – no Hb (diffusion)	100	~ 0	< 2
+ Hb (transport)	100	30	100
Carbon Dioxide (transport)	40	> 50	–

Abbreviations: Hb – hemoglobin; *pG* – partial pressure of gas

Carrier transport. In the face of the restrictions on diffusion imposed by membrane pores, the utilization of carrier mechanisms to facilitate passage of solutes across relatively impermeable membranes is teleologically understandable. Hemoglobin provides a familiar example of a carrier in an analogous situation (Table 5). The solubility of oxygen in plasma is so low that if tissues were supplied by dissolved oxygen alone, only 2% of normal tissue requirements would be met despite a very steep concentration gradient between lung and tissue. Addition of a carrier (hemoglobin) facilitates oxygen transport from lung to tissue more than 50-fold. The system exhibits typical features of carrier-mediated transport: saturation because of the finite number of carrier molecules available for transport at a given time, competition for and sharing of the carrier system by similar molecular species (oxygen and carbon dioxide), specificity since the system does not transport all gases, inhibition by some related molecules (carbon monoxide), and pathological (anemia) and genetic (sickle cell hemoglobin) variations.

The foregoing is an example of facilitated (or mediated) diffusion, involving no direct expenditure of metabolic energy upon the carrier system *per se*, to accomplish transport. A familiar transport system where direct energy expenditure is necessary is secretion from and reabsorption

Table 6. RENAL TUBULAR TRANSPORT (DOG)

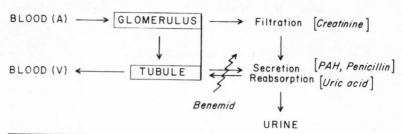

Compound	Transport Maximum T_m (mg/min)	Clearance Ratio * Relative to Creatinine
p-Aminohippurate (PAH)†	9.5	1.5
+ Benemid	1.0	1.0
Penicillin	265	4.25
+ Benemid	65	0.9
+ PAH	—	~ 1.0

Uric Acid	Mongrels	Dalmatians
Control	0.3	1.3
+ Benemid	0.5	0.8

* Clearance of test compound/clearance of Creatinine: C.R. = 1.0 = glomerular filtration only; C.R. < 1.0 = tubular reabsorption; C.R. > 1.0 = tubular secretion.

† Plasma: Tubule cell conc. gradient = 1:20.

References: 7-9

by renal tubules (Table 6). The tubular secretion of *para*-aminohippuric acid (PAH) represents transport from blood across the tubule cell to urine against a concentration gradient of blood = 1 to tubule cell = 20 in the study cited. Thus PAH must be carried "uphill" against the gradient. To do this, the tubule cell must expend energy derived from cellular oxidative metabolism. It was shown for the studies illustrated in Table 6 that interference with oxidative metabolism also interfered with PAH secretion (7-9). For this reason such transport is generally termed active or energy-linked transport. Again the characteristics of a carrier-mediated process are illustrated by a definite maximum rate (saturation), by competition of related molecules (PAH, penicillin, diodrast, PSP, etc.) for the carrier, specificity since other molecules like N-methyl nicotinamide are not transported by this system, and inhibition by a related compound (Benemid).

In addition the transport system is bi-directional, mediating the tubular reabsorption of uric acid from urine to blood. In this case a genetic difference between mongrel dogs and the Dalmatian strain is apparent (9). It should be noted that like most cases of solute transfer across membranes more than one process is utilized. Some PAH is transferred by diffusion across the glomerular membrane but the maximal rate is small (1.0 mg./min.) compared to the combined total of diffusion plus carrier-mediated transport across the tubule cell (9.5 mg./min.).

Transport of Carbohydrates and Amino Acid

With the foregoing principles in mind some typical cases of carrier transport for the two large classes of solutes, carbohydrates and amino acids, can be considered. Out of a wealth of material, the following have been chosen primarily to illustrate some important aspects of transport mechanisms and not necessarily for their typical nature.

Exchange diffusion of glycine by ascites cells. With the application of isotope tracer techniques to the study of transport processes, it soon became apparent that an important attribute of most carrier systems was the phenomenon of exchange diffusion, first described by Lundegårdh (90) and by Ussing (143, 144). A particularly good example taken from the studies of Heinz and collaborators (51-54) on mouse Ehrlich ascites tumor cells is shown in Table 7. In delineating this process Ussing (144) pointed out that as the concentration of solute is sufficiently increased, the carrier becomes saturated after which no *net* transfer across the membrane takes place, but provided the solute is freely available in both extracellular and intracellular phases, the flux of solute becomes equal in either direction with the solute-carrier complex able to exchange with another solute molecule on a one-to-one basis whenever the complex comes in contact with one or the other membrane boundary. The exchange rate is independent of the concentrations of solute but is limited by the number of solute-carrier complex molecules and their rate of diffusion across the confines of the membrane. In such a situation the carrier behaves, in Ussing's words, like a "ferryboat" or "shuttle."

The phenomenon can be "visualized" if the solute molecules in one fluid compartment are isotopically labelled, as in Table 7, for C^{14}-glycine and unlabelled glycine (represented in the diagram as S^* and S respectively). When the uptake rates of C^{14}-glycine into cells containing minimal contents of glycine are compared with uptake rates into cells preloaded with unlabelled glycine, the latter situation exhibits significantly higher rates

Table 7. EXCHANGE DIFFUSION OF AMINO ACIDS
(Mouse Ehrlich Ascites Tumor Cells)

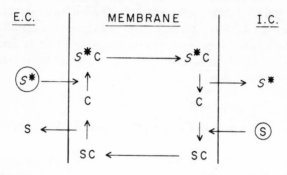

External Addition	Internal Preloading	Relative Uptake
Glycine-C¹⁴ (3 mM)	0	9.2
	Glycine (15 mM)	12.9
	N-acetylglycine (3 mM)	9.0
	Sarcosine (20 mM)	14.0
Sarcosine-C¹⁴ (3.5 mM)	0	3.6
	Glycine (15.5 mM)	6.1

	V_{max}
Glycine (Active transport)	10 μM/g/min
(Exchange)	57 μM/g/min

References: 51-54, 143, 144

because of carrier saturation and the occurrence of C¹⁴-glycine for un-labelled glycine (S^* for S) exchange diffusion. The process can involve autoexchange (glycine for glycine) and heteroexchange (glycine for sarco-sine [= methyl-glycine]) but is specific for carrier substrates, as indicated by the lack of effect of preloading with N-acetyl-glycine which does not share this carrier system. In the system illustrated in Table 7, the cells exhibit active (energy-linked) inward transport of glycine against a con-centration gradient, but as indicated the maximal rate of active inward transport was found to be only 20% of the rate of exchange diffusion ex-hibited by those cells once the carrier system was saturated.

This last point deserves special emphasis because failure to appreciate the rapidity of exchange diffusion in isotope studies may lead to erroneous interpretations of the characteristics of a particular transport system (143). On the other hand the process of exchange diffusion can be utilized to advantage in studies on cell processes by isotopically-labelled solutes where net penetration of such solutes across cell membranes is insufficient for ordinary analytical procedures. Two particularly good examples are the utilization of P^{32} exchange for studies on phosphate metabolism in bacteria by Mitchell (96) and of C^{14}-glutamic acid exchange across the blood-brain barrier for studies on cerebral glutamate metabolism by Lajtha *et al.* (81). In both cases the membranes in question behaved as if they were virtually impermeable to the externally added unlabelled solute (as judged by no demonstrable *net* uptake) but nevertheless rapidly exchanged sufficient labelled solute to permit metabolic studies.

Facilitated diffusion of glucose into muscle. Where carrier-mediated transport occurs in the absence of an opposing concentration gradient and exhibits no direct requirement for metabolic energy, the process is termed variously facilitated diffusion, mediated diffusion, facilitated transport, etc. The transfers of sugars across erythrocyte and skeletal muscle membranes represent typical examples of this type of transport mechanism. The data in Table 8 are taken from studies by Park and co-workers (97, 98, 112) on glucose uptake by perfused rat heart. Studies by Cori and co-workers on rat diaphragm and gastrocnemius have yielded similar data and interpretations (67, 68).

As outlined in Table 8, three steps in the utilization of glucose by muscle cells are envisaged: *diffusion* from plasma to muscle extracellular fluid, which was found to be rapid and not rate-limiting; *transport* across the cell membrane, which exhibited saturation kinetics, specificity, competition and other features characteristic of carrier mediation but operated equally well aerobically or anaerobically, hence was not directly energy-dependent; and *phosphorylation* by hexokinase with subsequent metabolism of the phosphorylated glucose to glycogen and via glycolysis. Park and co-workers were able to distinguish clearly between the latter two stages. At low external glucose concentrations transport was rate-limiting since the rate of delivery into the cell did not exceed the capacity of the phosphorylating system and no intracellular glucose could be detected (112). However, when the transport rate was markedly increased by addition of insulin (1 milliunit/ml. of perfusate), significant amounts of free intracellular glucose accumulated, indicating that the rate of transport was exceeding the rate of phosphorylation and the latter step had now become rate-limiting.

When data for normal rat heart muscle are compared with those for muscle from rats with alloxan-induced diabetes, in the absence of insulin the diabetic transport rate was only about one-third of normal. It is this factor which accounts for the well-known marked restriction of uptake of

Table 8. GLUCOSE TRANSPORT INTO CARDIAC MUSCLE
(Facilitated Diffusion)

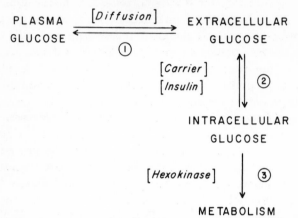

Perfused Rat Heart	Transport		Phosphorylation	
	K_t	V_{max}	K_p	V_{max}
	($\mu M/ml$)	($\mu M/g/hr$)	($\mu M/ml$)	($\mu M/g/hr$)
Normal	8.7	1.0	0.54	0.8
+ Insulin	27.8	5.0	0.54	0.8
Diabetic (Alloxan)	6.0	0.38	4.1	0.55
+ Insulin	27.8	5.0	4.1	0.55

K is an *inverse* measure of affinity of the transport carrier for glucose (K_t) or of hexokinase for glucose (K_p).

References: 97, 98, 112

glucose by untreated diabetic muscle (98). However, addition of insulin restored the transport system to normal and revealed another defect of diabetic muscle, an impaired rate of glucose phosphorylation (indicated by the elevation of the apparent K_p [Michaelis-Menten constant of hexokinase], signifying that much higher intracellular concentration of glucose was required to bring phosphorylation to normal rates). Insulin exerted no direct effect on phosphorylation by hexokinase in either normal or diabetic preparations. The impairment of phosphorylation exhibited by diabetic muscle may be attributable to elevated levels of glucose-6-phosphate (the product of the hexokinase reaction) derived from excess glycogen degradation (98). Glucose-6-phosphate is an established noncompetitive inhibitor of the hexokinase reaction (21, 22). A somewhat analogous effect has been attributed to the action of epinephrine which is associated with glycogen breakdown and inhibition of muscle glucose phosphorylation (68).

The action of insulin in enhancing glucose transport was first recognized by Levine *et al.* (85) and has been amply confirmed. There is a general consensus that the primary action of insulin is an acceleration of carbohydrate transport across insulin-sensitive membranes. This may not be the only action of insulin (67, 77), and this particular action is not very specific for individual sugars (67) or even for carbohydrates, since comparable effects on transport of some, but not all, amino acids across insulin-sensitive membranes have been demonstrated (46, 69, 92). Although the precise mode of action of insulin on carbohydrate transport remains to be elucidated, its primary action is superficially at least analogous to effects of the antidiuretic hormone in that insulin seems to make more transport facilities available.

Obviously the reaction sequence of glucose entry into muscle does not terminate with intracellular delivery (Table 8), since normally all that is delivered is promptly removed by phosphorylation and further metabolism. This aspect deserves emphasis because it is typical of a common complication of the study of membrane transport mechanisms for most solutes of metabolic interest and has led to the use of various non-metabolizable "model" compounds for study of the transport process only. Results with the latter have not always been helpful since metabolically "inert" substitutes may not be typical or universal models for the process being evaluated (46). It should also be appreciated that metabolic removal of the transported solute creates a concentration gradient in the inward direction which would not necessarily reveal the operation of a carrier-mediated transport system underlying an *apparent* diffusion process along the gradient. An additional complication of the metabolic removal factor is that it may obscure the interpretation of the type of transport mechanism operating, since metabolic "trapping" of inflowing solute renders the system apparently uni-directional when in fact it may be bi-directional (144).

The characteristics of carbohydrate transport across the erythrocyte membrane closely resemble those found for skeletal muscle (83, 112, 120, 155) with the exception that the red cell membrane is not sensitive to insulin. This latter exception applies to a number of other cell membranes, including the blood-brain barrier (110) and probably neural cells themselves (55, 114). Le Fevre (84) has calculated for the erythrocyte that the maximum number of sugar transport sites in the membrane is of the order of 500,000 per red cell "ghost" or about 10 μM of sites/kg. of cells, which is of the same order as suggested for ion transport sites. He estimated that in full operation of glucose transport the minimum turnover at each site would be about 500 per second, or about 18 mM/g/hr. Of all mammalian cells studied only those of the intestinal mucosa (4, 5, 20) and kidney (128) exhibit active, energy-linked transport against concentration gradients (19). It is of some interest that the transport of carbohydrates across intestinal mucosa is clearly dependent upon the presence of sodium ions (10, 19, 23).

Active transport of galactose by E. Coli mutants. The most complex transport systems are those which are "active" or directly energy-dependent. The unravelling of the details of such systems has been assisted by such studies as those by Monod and associated on genetic mutants of *E. Coli* (18, 64). An example illustrating galactose transport by mutants lacking the final phosphorylation (galactokinase) step is given in Table 9. The characteristics of active inward transport are summarized in the upper half of the table: transport against a concentration gradient (1:2700), energy dependence, competition for the carrier and pronounced specificity (not illustrated), and active exchange diffusion. The lower half of the table illustrates the effects of varying the culture medium on the entry and exit reactions of the transport process. Compared to the active, energy-dependent inward transport, the exit process behaves as a facilitated diffusion type of transport. The independent manipulation of these two processes clearly illustrates their relative contributions to the equilibrium or steady-state balance between entry and exit. Cohen and Monod (18) have suggested the term *permease* to identify the mechanisms responsible for each

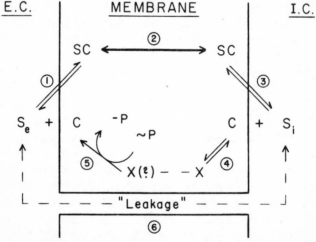

Fig. 4.   Proposed scheme for active, energy-dependent carrier transport across cell membranes, modified from Heinz and Walsh (54). The numbers refer to stages in the process discussed in the text. *Abbreviations*: E.C.—extracellular. I.C.—intracellular. S_e and S_i—solute in extracellular (e) and intracellular (i) fluid spaces. C—membrane carrier. SC—solute-carrier complex. X—inactivated form of carrier. $\sim$P—metabolically derived energy as energy-rich phosphate. -P—inorganic phosphate left after energy transfer to the carrier regeneration reaction.

Table 9. ACTIVE TRANSPORT OF GALACTOSE BY *E. Coli* MUTANTS

A. *Inward Transport*

Conditions	Equilibrium Cellular Accumulation	Significance
Medium Galactose (2×10^{-5} M)	6×10^{-2} M	Ratio I/E = 2700
+ 2,4-DNP (10^{-3} M)	10% of control	Energy dependent
+ Glucose (equi-M)	2X control	Energy dependent
+ L-Arabinose (equi-M)	60% of control	Carrier competition
Medium C^{14}-galactose (2×10^{-4} M)	C^{14} = 18 μM/g at 20 min.	Free I.C.; Steady-state
+ C^{12}-galactose (10^{-2} M) at 20 min.	C^{14} = 1 μM/g at 40 min.	Balance: in = out.

B. *Manipulation of Entry and Exit Reactions*

Growth Medium	Entry Rate (μM/g/min)	Exit Rate (k_e)*	Equilibrium Accumulation (μM/g)	Significance
Succinate 0.4%	3.0	(0.11)	27.7	Increased
+ Galactose 10^{-5} M	3.1	(0.52)	5.9	exit rate
Mannose 0.4%	4.5	(0.19)	23.8	Decreased
Mannose 0.2%				entry rate
+ Glucose 0.2%	1.6	(0.19)	8.4	
Succinate 0.4% + Galactose 10^{-5} M	3.8	(0.9)	4.2	Inhibition
Incubated with				of exit
Succinate 0.025 M	4.1	(0.14)	28.3	

*Exit expressed as first order rate constant (k_e)

Reference: 64

of these transport processes. Analogous mechanisms for bacterial uptake of other carbohydrates, amino acids, and other solutes have also been demonstrated (18, 37).

Figure 4 summarizes schematically much of what has been discussed so far. The diagram has been adapted from Heinz and Walsh (54), who designed it for the ascites cell transport of glycine, but a very similar scheme for *E. Coli* sugar transport has been proposed by Kepes (66) and many others can be found throughout the transport literature.

In such a complete system there are at least six component reactions. Active inward transport involves the first five: *1,* combination of the extracellular solute (S) with the active carrier (C) to form the solute-carrier complex (SC); 2, diffusion of this complex across the transport region within the membrane; 3, dissociation at the inner side of this region releasing the solute (S) intracellularly; 4, simultaneous catalytic inactivation of the carrier to some other form (X); and 5, regeneration of new carrier by the expenditure of metabolic energy (usually derived from cellular oxidative metabolism and supplied as energy-rich phosphate, $\sim P$). Obviously it is steps 4 and 5 which make transport against a concentration gradient possible, since inactivation of the carrier at the inner membrane boundary provides less opportunity for intracellular solute to re-complex with the carrier and travel outward, but at the same time new carrier must be generated at the outer membrane boundary to bring inward additional external solute. These two reactions presumably relate to the entry and exit *permease* reactions discussed in Table 9 (64, 66).

As the intracellular concentration of solute rises, exchange diffusion will occur, involving primarily steps 1-3, each of which must be partially reversible. Thus, at saturation of the carrier system exchanges of incoming solute for outgoing solute will become rapid (cf. Table 7). Presumably step 4 must also be partially reversible or modifiable (54) to permit a reasonable rate of exchange diffusion. By omitting steps 4 and 5, the scheme in Figure 4 will fit a facilitated diffusion process. A final component of most such systems is passive diffusion or "leakage" across the membrane (step 6) in the direction of the concentration gradient.

Thus, as Ussing (144) has pointed out, the penetration of substances across a membrane is usually resolvable into three terms: a free or passive diffusion term, an exchange diffusion term (one-to-one exchange without energy expenditure), and an active transport term (where the carrier "disappears" at one boundary letting fewer carriers return than are arriving).

Transport across Neural Membranes

Carbohydrates. The concentrations of glucose in cerebrospinal fluid (CSF) and in brain tissue are similar at about 4 mM (~ 70 mg/100 ml) and slightly less than the blood glucose concentration of about 5 mM (~ 90 mg/100 ml) (63, 139). In normal ranges small variations of blood glucose levels are reflected by proportionate changes in CSF levels. But when blood levels are increased to abnormally high values, as in untreated diabetes mellitus, a maximum CSF level becomes apparent (63). Experimentally Geiger (38) in studies on the perfused cat brain *in vivo* found that at a cerebral perfusate glucose level of about 45 mM ($\sim$800 mg/100 ml), the brain concentration was only about 15 mM ($<$300 mg/100 ml), and failed to increase significantly above that when the perfusate concentration was raised to 90 mM. Such behavior of CSF and brain glucose levels is compatible with carrier-mediated transport into the brain exhibiting characteristic saturation.

This interpretation is also suggested by the *in vivo* studies on rat heart and brain by Park *et al.* (110) summarized in Table 10. The data are referred to the distribution of mannitol, an indicator of extracellular space resembling glucose in terms of molecular size and configuration but failing to penetrate muscle cell membranes. The effect on muscle of insulin in increasing cellular penetration of all sugars tested (except ribose which is not transported by a carrier system in muscle) is consistent with concepts already discussed (Table 8). Under these same conditions two contrasts are provided by brain. Insulin was without any significant effect on the tissue/plasma distribution ratios, and three compounds (mannitol, fructose and ribose) were essentially excluded from brain fluids as judged by the chloride space figure. The lack of a direct effect of insulin on brain glucose under these conditions has long been recognized (55), and suggests that the membranes associated with the blood-brain barrier mechanism are insulin-insensitive. Furthermore exclusion of some of the test sugars attests to the operation of the barrier mechanism and suggests that there is some selectivity or specificity in the types of sugars able to traverse the membranes concerned. Such a phenomenon would also be consistent with a carrier transport system across the barrier.

A similar *in vitro* comparison is given in Table 10, illustrating the significant response of rat heart muscle to low doses of insulin (97) but only a questionable response of rat cerebral cortex to insulin at 100 times the effective muscle dose (114). This latter effect was statistically significant, but since it was not elicitable from cortical slices without adhering pia-arachnoid (2nd slices), since it required a relatively large dose of insulin, and since it failed to affect glucose metabolism (114) (contrary to marked increases demonstrable in muscle [112]), the interpretation for cerebral cortex slices is difficult. In these studies on rat cerebral cortex, cerebellum and spinal cord Rafaelsen (114) laid stress on the "intactness" of the tissue sample as a prerequisite for demonstrating an effect of added insulin, but it is difficult to reconcile this concept with the fact that the majority of neural cells under optimal *in vitro* conditions maintain resting membrane potentials at or near normal (87) as well as a normal medium to tissue distribution of electrolytes and amino acids (137, 138)—all attesting to functionally intact cellular membranes. It seems reasonable to conclude that neural cell membranes are relatively insulin-insensitive on direct exposure to unusually large doses of insulin. In view of the heterogeneity of brain tissue, the possibility that one cellular element (glial or endothelial) might respond to insulin whereas the others do not, deserves con-

Table 10. CARBOHYDRATE TRANSPORT – INSULIN EFFECT

A. *In Vivo*

| | [Tissue/Plasma Ratio] | | |
| | Rat Heart | | Rat Brain |
	Control	+ Insulin	± Insulin
Chloride	–	–	0.3
Mannitol	0.22	0.22	0.03
D-Glucose*	0.19	0.64	0.4
D-Galactose	–	–	0.6
D-Fructose	0.18	0.55	0.03
L-Arabinose*	0.27	0.63	0.4
D-Ribose	0.25	0.37†	0.03

* Comparable data for D-Mannose and D-Xylose
† Difference not significant

B. *In Vitro*

| | | [Glucose Uptake – $\mu M/g/hr$] | |
| | | Incubated Rat Cerebral Cortex‡ | |
	Perfused Rat Heart§	1st Slice	2nd Slice
Glucose (16.7 $\mu M/ml$)	10.0	8.7	9.95
+ Insulin (10^{-3} U/ml) % of control	140%	100%	–
+ Insulin (10^{-1} U/ml) % of control	–	113.5%	100%

‡ Uncorrected for extracellular glucose
§ Free intracellular glucose: control 0; + Insulin 5.3 $\mu M/ml$.

References: 97, 110, 114

sideration. It should be pointed out that Rafaelsen (114) determined glucose disappearance from the medium as the measure of tissue uptake, but without direct determinations of the presence or absence of free tissue glucose the significance of the uptake figures is not clear.

There is some evidence compatible with a glucose transport system across neural cell membranes (Table 11). In rat diaphragm *in vitro* Kipnis and Cori (67) demonstrated that 2-deoxyglucose competes with glucose for inward transport, and it has also been established that they also compete for hexokinase in many tissues, including brain (22, 131). Data illustrating the effects of 2-deoxyglucose on glucose uptake and distribution in cat cerebral cortex slices (136) are given in Table 11. By analogy with the results obtained on muscle by Kipnis and Cori (67), it may be concluded

Table 11. CAT CEREBRAL CORTEX GLUCOSE UPTAKE
(Slices incubated aerobically 1 hr. in bicarbonate saline)

Medium Additions	Final Medium Conc. ($\mu M/ml$)	Total Net Uptake ($\mu M/g/hr$)	Free IC Conc. * ($\mu M/ml$)	IC Conc. as Hexose-P ($\mu M/ml$)
Glucose (10 mM)	5.65	37.9	0	< 1.2
Glucose (10 mM)	7.5	17.05	3.9	< 1.6
+ 2-deoxyglucose (10 mM)	8.5	6.05	5.6	7.3

*Net glucose or 2-DG spaces (corrected for slice swelling which was confined to chloride and sucrose spaces):

[Per cent]

	Chloride; Sucrose	Glucose	2-DG	Swelling
Control	35.5	10	–	65.7
+ 2-DG	46.5	67	71	55.3

Calculated from data of Tower (136)

that the accumulation of free, intracellular glucose and 2-deoxyglucose in the cortical slices, when both are present in equimolar contractions externally, is consistent with a carrier-mediated mechanism for glucose transfer into neural cells.*

None of the evidence cited here represents conclusive proof of specific, carrier-mediated transport across neural membranes, although much is compatible with such a process. The crucial experiments remain to be done. Before leaving the subject mention should be made of the studies by Geiger and Yamasaki (39) on the perfused cat brain *in vivo*. When the liver was omitted from the perfusion circuit, aerobic glycolysis developed followed by impermeability of the brain to glucose with a reduction of brain survival time to about an hour. Inclusion of the liver in the perfusion circuit prevented such developments up to 4 to 5 hours, and could be replaced by addition of small amounts of the nucleosides, cytidine and uridine, to the perfusate. The significance of these observations is not

* The cerebral cortex studies by Tower (136) cited in Table 11 and those on muscle by Kipnis and Cori (67), aside from the species difference, are not entirely comparable, since the latter study utilized a phosphate-saline incubation medium whereas the cerebral cortex studies were conducted in bicarbonate-saline where inorganic phosphate availability would be a limiting factor owing to its sequestration as non-metabolizable 2-deoxyglucose-6-phosphate (136).

clear, but they also suggest a carrier-mediated transport system for cerebral glucose which may exhibit special supportive requirements.

Amino acids. The composition of the free amino acid pool in the central nervous system is quite distinctive compared to most other mammalian tissues (135, 137, 150, 153), so that it is not surprising to find that amino acid transport across neural membranes differs in some cases from that found elsewhere in the body. Because of the obvious heterogeneity of the amino acid group—some basic, some acidic, most neutral; some "essential" (supplied only from dietary intake) and some synthesized by cells *in situ;* some prominent in free pools of tissue participating actively in intermediary metabolism and some only minimally present free but concerned primarily with protein synthesis and turnover—it is not possible to treat amino acids as a group in terms of transport mechanisms (as is usually possible with common monosaccharides), and the findings relevant for one amino acid may not apply to others. Nevertheless, it is probably fair to say that in the central nervous system the transport aspects of amino acids have more in common than in most other body tissues.

A good example of the differences between brain and other tissues in transport characteristics for amino acids is provided by the studies of Udenfriend and co-workers on the uptake of tyrosine by rat tissues (14, 45, 47), summarized in Table 12. Tyrosine is representative of the aromatic group of natural and "essential" amino acids, and since its rate of metabolic utilization was minimal under the conditions employed, an uncomplicated study of cellular uptake processes was possible. It is obvious that only brain exhibited active (energy-dependent) transport of tyrosine against a concentration gradient by a relatively specific system exhibiting competitive characteristics. In other tissues the data seemed most compatible with passive diffusion rather than carrier-mediated transport. A difference between brain *in vivo* and *in vitro* is apparent in that D-tyrosine and *para*-hydroxyphenylacetic acid were virtually excluded from brain *in vivo* while both penetrated brain slices *in vitro,* D-tyrosine being actively transported in this case. Guroff *et al.* (47) concluded that these differences between brain *in vivo* and *in vitro* were probably attributable to two components of tyrosine transport in neural tissues: one across the blood-brain barrier facilitating L-tyrosine uptake and exhibiting structural and steric specificity, and the other across neural cell membranes requiring energy and subject to competition but not steric specificity.

The above results are consistent with previous observations on a number of other amino acids (Table 13). The first evidence for active (energy-dependent) transport of an amino acid against a concentration gradient in brain was reported by Stern *et al.* (132) for L-glutamic acid *in vitro.* Some of their results are given in Table 13 (B-1a). Their findings were subse-

Table 12. AMINO ACID TRANSPORT – NEURAL vs. NON-NEURAL
(Tyrosine)

Additions	[Tissue conc./External conc. Ratio]				
	Brain		Muscle	Liver	Kidney
	In Vivo	In Vitro*	In Vitro	In Vitro	In Vitro
L-Tyrosine (1 mM)	1.3	1.75	0.74†	0.66	1.13
+ Glucose (20 mM)	–	2.6	0.81	0.68	1.15
+ 2,4-DNP (1 mM)	–	1.07	–	0.78	1.01
+ L-Tryptophan (equi-M) % of control	30%	47%	100%	–	–
+ p-Fluorophenylalanine (equi-M) % of control	30%	33%	–	–	–
D-Tyrosine (1 mM)	<0.5	1.7	0.55	–	–
p-OH-phenylacetic acid (1 mM)	0.0	0.65	0.4	–	–
+ Glucose (20 mM)	–	0.65	–	–	–

* Not corrected for extracellular fraction (including slice swelling). Calculated ratio of intracellular/extracellular conc.: L-Tyrosine 2.73; + glucose
4.63. Corresponding figures for muscle are 0.9 and 0.9 and for brain p-OH-
phenylacetic acid (± glucose) 0.87.

† No change on addition of insulin.

References: 14, 45-47

quently confirmed by Takagaki *et al.* (134) and extended to include D-
glutamic acid (Table 13, B-1b). This latter study also drew attention to
the absolute dependence of glutamic acid active transport on the presence
of external sodium ions, an observation reminiscent of a similar finding for
active sugar transport across intestinal mucosa (10, 19, 23). In both the
glutamic acid (132) and tyrosine (47) studies the effect of increasing external amino acid concentration on the tissue/medium ratio was to decrease
the latter to a minimal value of about 2.0, a phenomenon which would
seem most explicable in terms of carrier saturation although it cannot be
excluded that high external concentrations may tax the carrier regenerating
system in the face of a presumably high rate of exchange diffusion (cf.
Fig. 4).

The two sets of glutamic acid data discussed above are expressed as
tissue/medium ratios rather than as ratios of concentrations in the two
fluid spaces concerned. An indication of the latter in cat cerebral cortex
(140) is shown in Table 13 (B-2) for "endogenous" ratios. Leakage from
the incubated slices into the incubation medium has been utilized as the

Table 13. GLUTAMIC ACID TRANSPORT IN BRAIN

A. *In Vivo (Rats)*

		Plasma ($\mu M/ml$)	[Tissue/Plasma Ratio]*			
			Brain	Muscle	Liver	Kidney
1. i.v. Glutamic acid Control		0.2	51.2	6.0	16.7	32.7
(plasma level 10m post-inj.		7.4				
30-50X (a) *Theory* if						
normal) impermeable			(1.4)	(0.16)	(0.46)	(0.9)
(b) *Found*			1.3†	0.8	1.4	3.7
2. i.v. C^{14}-Glutamic acid		(cpm/ml)				
(plasma level						
< 2X normal) 5m post-inj.		1120	0.415	0.43	5.3	5.1

*For C^{14} data ratio expressed as (cpm/g) tissue/(cpm/ml) plasma *in* glutamic acid — as calculated from glutamic acid S.A. (cpm/μM) and organ conc./g — and corrected for organ blood activity.

†No change in brain level up to 60 min. post-injection.

(*Table continued on next page.*)

basis for estimating the steady-state concentration gradient maintained: aerobically slice/medium (both as $\mu M/ml$. fluid space) $= 100/1$, while under partial anaerobiosis the ratio fell to $10/1$. Comparable results were obtained with C^{14}-labelled L-glutamic acid added to the medium as an indicator of exchange diffusion under these conditions. The magnitude of aerobically maintained intracellular/extracellular ratios here, while higher than in most other mammalian tissues studied *in vitro,* is not at all exceptional, since Horecker *et al.* (64) reported ratios in excess of $2700/1$ for galactose in *E. Coli.*

The *in vitro* data may be compared with *in vivo* studies reported by Waelsch and associates (81, 126) and shown in Table 13 (A). Elevations of *in vivo* plasma levels of glutamic acid to 30-50 times normal failed to influence brain levels whereas significant rises of glutamic acid levels in other body tissues were observed (126). Under comparable circumstances administration of the amide of glutamic acid, glutamine, results in significant entry of the amide into the central nervous system (126, 137). Clearly the blood-brain barrier is essentially impermeable to glutamic acid in terms of *net uptake,* a finding which fits well with evidence that the majority of cerebral glutamate is metabolically derived from cerebral glucose (137, 149). On the other hand rapid *exchange* of C^{14}-labelled glutamic acid clearly occurs across the barrier, as shown in the table. As Lajtha (80) points out, it is difficult to explain inhibition of net uptake while

Table 13. GLUTAMIC ACID TRANSPORT IN BRAIN (Continued)

B. *In Vitro*

1. Guinea Pig Cerebral Cortex Slices

Conditions	Medium Conc. (μM/ml) Initial	Final	Final (40-60 min) Slice/Medium Ratio (μM/g or ml)
(a) Bicarbonate-saline			
L-Glutamic acid + glucose	2.5	1.3	19.4
	5.0	4.0	6.5
	10.0	8.25	4.0
	20.0	18.0	2.3
(b) Phosphate-saline			
L-Glutamic acid	10.0	–	2.3
+ Glucose			5.55
Sodium-free + glucose			0.8
Potassium-free + glucose			2.05
D-Glutamic acid	10.0	–	0.95
+ Glucose			5.05
+ Glucose + Azide			2.15
+ Glucose + Iodoacetate			3.1

2. Cat Cerebral Cortex Slices

Conditions	Endogenous Medium Conc. (μM/ml) Initial	Final	Steady State (1 hr) Slice IC μM/ml / Medium μM/ml
(a) Normal Slices:			
Aerobic, glucose	0.55	0.3	100
10% O_2, glucose	0.6	0.8	10
	Medium** Final cpm/ml		Slice IC cpm †† / Medium cpm
(b) + C[14]-Glutamic acid (1 μM)	32000		34.7

** SA of medium = SA of slice glutamic acid

†† For free glutamic acid only. Tissue free glutamic acid = 40% of total uptake (remainder metabolized).

References: *81, 126, 132, 134, 140*

rapid exchange can occur unless one invokes other than a purely passive diffusion process.

Findings quite analogous to those for glutamic acid (Table 13) have been reported for γ-aminobutyric acid (27, 28, 142), lysine (78, 82), and leucine (79) which altogether provide examples for neutral (γ-aminobutyrate and leucine), dicarboxylic (glutamate) and diamino (lysine) groups of amino acids. In addition there are a number of more recent studies by Dr. Abel Lajtha on active transport of various amino acids in *both* directions across the blood-brain barrier (80).

Comparable studies on other tissues indicate considerable variability in modes of amino acid uptake. A number of amino acids, notably glutamic acid, γ-aminobutyric acid, lysine and tyrosine, do not appear to be actively transported into muscle (28, 45, 92, 132) whereas others, notably alanine and glycine are actively transported (92). Transport across intestinal mucosa is active against a concentration gradient, stereospecific and competitive for most amino acids, but again there are exceptions, notably glutamic acid and lysine (1, 2, 36, 101, 158, 159). Kidney may probably be classed with intestine (72) whereas liver tends to resemble muscle (28, 132) in amino acid transport characteristics. From this brief survey there seems little doubt that in the central nervous system transport mechanisms are abundant and in some cases relatively unique for the transfer of amino acids across the various neural membranes.

Other molecules. If the blood-brain barrier mechanism functions as a membrane with carrier-mediated transport activities, exit as well as entry transfers of solutes should be demonstrable. Lajtha (80) has obtained such evidence for active transport of amino acids from CSF to blood. Richmond and Hastings (116) have reached similar conclusions for their studies on the anion, sulfate. And in Table 14 comparable data for Diodrast (and PSP —not illustrated) are shown, as reported by Pappenheimer *et al.* (108). Using goats with a ventriculo-cisternal perfusion system, they studied the relative rates of entry (blood $\rightarrow$ CSF) and exit (CSF $\rightarrow$ blood) for solutes exhibiting passive diffusion only (creatinine, fructose, inulin) and for the test compounds Diodrast and phenolsulfonphthalein. The latter entered CSF from blood very poorly but were rapidly transported out of CSF into blood even against a concentration gradient (Table 14). Inhibition of the exit transport process by *para*-aminohippurate (PAH) and the fact that Diodrast, PSP and PAH behave similarly in renal tubular secretion (Table 6) clearly implicate an analogous carrier-mediated transport system for their exit from CSF. By comparison with muscle, the effect of molecular size on passive diffusion appears to be less of a factor for blood to CSF passage and evidence at high solute concentrations for bulk transfers across the barrier membranes was observed (108).

Even very large molecules can penetrate from blood into CSF over a period of time, as illustrated in Table 15. Isotopically-labelled albumen (molecular weight approximately 70,000, compared to glucose = 180; glutamic acid = 147) entered the CSF relatively rapidly and achieved equilibration between CSF and plasma in less than 24 hours (33). The very

Table 14. TRANSPORT INTO AND OUT OF CSF
(Goat — ventriculo-cisternal)

Compound	MW.	Clearance (ml/min)*		
		Blood → CSF	CSF → Blood	Blood → Muscle
Diodrast	405	0.04	0.71†	–
Inulin	~ 500	–	0.12	0.02
Fructose	180	0.13	0.17	–
Creatinine	113	0.21	0.19	0.3
Diodrast		[2:1]▲	0.23	
+ PAH			− 0.14	

*Vol. of blood or CSF cleared of compound in 1 min.

†V_{max} = 2-3 µg/min (saturation kinetics) compared to renal V_{max} = 50-200 µg/min per g.

▲Transport against a concentration gradient blood/CSF of 2:1 and inhibition by p-amino-hippurate (PAH).

Reference: 108

much larger γ-globulin molecule also gains access to CSF from plasma, albeit much more slowly and apparently without attaining equilibrium (129).*

The blood-brain barrier mechanism. A considerable number of data have been discussed here indicating carrier-mediated transport across the barrier mechanism as well as reemphasizing the restrictions imposed by this mechanism on *in vivo* distribution of solutes contrasted with their *in vitro* distribution between plasma and neural cells. The transport studies in particular would seem to be most cogent arguments for a distinct membrane-like mechanism. One cannot help but be intrigued by the possibility that many of the "barrier" attributes of this mechanism in keeping out or limiting the entry of many solutes may relate to active transport systems in the barrier "membrane" operating primarily in the exit direction (brain or CSF → blood), as is found for certain amino acids, sulfate, and Diodrast discussed above. There are, of course, good precedents for "exit" transport in the case of sodium extrusion from cells and in the operation of the renal tubule transport systems. Pappenheimer *et al.* (108) have

* The latter conclusion requires some reservations because the patient studied had both hypogammaglobulinemia and Friedreich's ataxia and hence may not represent the normal situation in the context under discussion. Furthermore if part of CSF γ-globulin were endogenously derived from the central nervous system, equilibrium of total CSF γ-globulin with plasma γ-globulin under these conditions would not be expected.

Table 15. PROTEIN TRANSFER INTO CSF

	Time of Appearance in CSF after injection	Equilibrium Time CSF : Plasma *
I^{131}-Albumen (Dog)†	~ 40 min.	17 - 25 hrs.
I^{131}-γ-Globulin (Man)	> 10 hrs.	None
		(peak time: ~ 6 days; $SA_{csf} \sim 0.5\ SA_{plasma}$)

* Both in terms of SA (cpm/mg total protein)
† Mol. wt. about 70000.

References: 33, 129

called attention to a potentially practical aspect of this concept by suggesting that penicillin, which shares the Diodrast-PAH renal tubule transport system (cf. Table 6) may be excluded from the central nervous system by the exit transport system exemplified by Diodrast (Table 14) and that on this analogy a compound such as Benemid, which inhibits the analogous renal transport process, might make it possible to achieve therapeutic levels of penicillin in the central nervous system from systemic rather than from the presently necessary intrathecal administration.

The transport data would seem to establish beyond doubt the blood-brain barrier as functional mechanism regardless of still unsolved morphological problems or of previous studies whose physiological and/or methodological pertinence may be questioned (26). It is to be regretted that a current review of the subject (26) rather overlooked the evidence available on transport and tended to adopt a rather negative attitude toward the whole barrier question, just at the time when so much positive data on the barrier is becoming apparent. A forthcoming review by Lajtha (80) provides what seems to be a more reasonable discussion of the subject. From the latter the barrier emerges as a functional and selective bi-directional set of transport mechanisms situated at the portals to the central nervous system.

Specialized Transport Mechanisms

Pinocytosis and phagocytosis. Pinocytosis is characteristic of primitive cells like the amoeba but can be observed in many more highly differentiated cells under appropriate conditions and has many features in common with phagocytosis. The cell membrane of the amoeba is impermeable to glucose and the presence of glucose alone in the surrounding fluid does

Table 16. PHAGOCYTOSIS
(Guinea Pig Leukocytes)

	Resting	Phagocytizing
Oxygen consumption (Q_{O_2})	18.7	45.6
Glucose consumption (μM/30 min)	1.2	1.1
Lactic acid production (μM/30 min)	1.9	2.6
CO_2 from glucose (C1/C6 ratio)	8.1	21.6
% glucose via HMP shunt	3-6	20-40
Lipid – P (SA P^{32} – relative)	(100)	(182)
Granules present	+	0
Granule enzymes free in cytoplasm	0	+

References: 56, 65, 123, 124

not stimulate pinocytosis. However when pinocytosis is stimulated (*e.g.*, by adding protein to the medium) glucose is taken up with the pinocytotic droplets in significant quantities and enters cellular metabolism with most of it eventually recoverable as carbon dioxide (13). On the basis of observations of neural cells in tissue culture (70, 111), the suggestion has been made that neural cells, among others, may utilize pinocytosis as a means of taking in molecules from the surrounding medium (70). No decision for or against this possibility can be made on the basis of present evidence, but several drawbacks to a pinocytotic type of mechanism of transport in highly differentiated cells in an organized tissue can be mentioned. As Ussing (145) points out, uptake of droplets of environmental fluid by pinocytosis into the cytoplasm results in equivalent transport of *all* solutes in the fluid medium into the cell and fails to account for uni-directional transport, differences in diffusion and transport rates, or differential distribution of ions and other solutes. Furthermore, since the process of pinocytosis involves an infolding of the outer cellular membrane around the fluid droplet and subsequent pinching off as a cytoplasmic, membrane-enclosed vacuole, Chapman-Andresen and Holter (13) point out that such a vacuolar membrane would be expected to retain its selective permeability properties for some time and could not be assumed *a priori* to be more permeable than it originally was simply by virtue of its shift in location.

The closely analogous process of phagocytosis is, of course, utilized by a number of cell types in various mammalian tissues, *e.g.*, leukocytes, macrophages, and the microglia of the nervous system. Considerable information is now available on the morphological and biochemical aspects of this process in leukocytes. Morphologically it has been observed that a pseudopod of cytoplasm gradually engulfs the particle (bacterium, starch granule, etc.) to be phagocytized until it is completely enclosed as a vacuole-like structure within the cytoplasm surrounded by a membrane-like rim (42, 43). Coincident with phagocytic ingestion of the particle, the leukocyte exhibits a pronounced loss of its characteristic cytoplasmic granules, the degree of loss being proportional to the amount of material phagocytized (56). Coincident with both the foregoing sets of phenomena, striking alterations in the metabolic characteristics of the leukocyte have been demonstrated by Sbarra and Karnovsky (123, 124), as indicated in Table 16. Not only is there an increased rate of metabolism (Q_{0_2}), presumably related to the additional energy requirements for phagocytosis, but there is a shift in metabolic emphasis from glucolysis via the Embden-Meyerhof glycolytic pathway to glucose oxidation via the hexose-monophosphate (HMP) shunt or direct oxidative pathway (yielding an increased C1/C6 ratio) plus an increased rate of lactic acid production without a concomitant increase of glucose utilization. Sbarra and Karnovsky have suggested that this metabolic shift may in part reflect a requirement for additional membrane synthesis. The enhanced turnover of various precursors of membrane lipid constituents, such as lipid-P^{32}, are compatible with such a possibility. The degranulation phenomenon noted above appears to be related to the release from the cytoplasmic granules of lytic enzymes (? lysozyme) for digestion of the phagocytized particles (56) as well as other enzymes possibly related to some of the metabolic shifts just discussed (65). These complex reactions which appear to be necessary concomitants of phagocytosis would seem to render transport processes of this type unsuitable for transferring ordinary small molecular weight solutes across cell membranes and to require specific cells specialized for phagocytosis.

Virus invasion. Most viruses exhibit a biphasic life cycle, a free-living phase during which they are infective, and a parasitic phase within the infected host cell during which virus progeny are propagated. Entry of the virus particle into host cells for the latter purpose is a complex process, best exemplified perhaps by the infection of *E. Coli* cells by bacteriophage viruses. Kozloff and co-workers (74-76) have distinguished four stages in bacteriophage invasion: *1*, adsorption of the virus, tail-first, to the cell wall at specific zinc-containing protein sites in the latter; *2*, hydrolytic alteration of the virus tail structure by the zinc-protein, causing the tail to contract or shorten (mediated by an actomyosin-like contractile protein in the virus tail); *3*, upon shortening, a lytic enzyme (lysozyme) present in the proximal tail is brought in contact with the host-cell wall and digests a portion of the latter (releasing up to 15% of the total nitrogen and 5% of the total carbon in the host-cell wall); and *4*, as a result, specific cell wall constituents, such as lysine or hexosamine, are exposed which trigger an almost instantaneous injection of virus deoxyribonucleic acid (DNA) from the virus head into the host-cell cytoplasm. The viral DNA once within the host cell possesses the capacity as the genetic determinant to reorganize host-cell metabolism exclusively for replication of viral proteins, DNA, etc., thus ensuring propagation of the virus.

Other types of viruses apparently utilize analogous mechanisms for invasion of host cells. Notable is a group including several neurotropic viruses (*e.g.*, influenza virus) which attach to host-cell membranes by specific "receptors," the surface available N-acetyl-neuraminic acid moieties of ganglioside or ganglioside-like molecules present in host-cell membranes (44, 71, 74). The process of attachment involves splitting off of the neuraminic acid moiety by a specific neuraminidase enzyme contained in the virus coat. Since in most ganglioside-type structures a hexosamine moiety is immediately subadjacent to the neuraminic acid, this is then exposed in close proximity to the attached virus. On analogy from the bacteriophage studies, it has been suggested that hexosamine in this situation also triggers release of viral DNA into the host cell, and some experimental evidence for this mechanism has been reported (11).

Undoubtedly there are many specialized mechanisms for transferring special substances across otherwise impermeable membranes. The two foregoing examples are perhaps sufficiently exotic to indicate the potential range of possibilities.

Carriers and Receptors

With few exceptions the precise nature and mode of operation of carriers, receptors and related units in cell membranes remain to be elucidated. It is beyond the scope of this discussion to review the many possibilities which have been proposed, but a few which at present seem reasonable and/or promising have been collected in Table 17.

The pyridine nucleotides (DPN and TPN) and hemoglobin are well characterized cellular units in the transport of metabolically-derived hydrogen atoms and of oxygen or carbon dioxide respectively. These and other comparable systems represent some prototypes for the more speculative possibilities listed in Table 17.

Various lipid components common to membrane structure have been suggested as carriers or receptors. Phosphatidic acid and/or phosphoinositides have been proposed by Hokin and Hokin (59-61) as the carrier moieties for sodium ion transport in various tissues, including brain, and for certain cellular secretions such as pancreatic zymogen, with the phos-

Table 17. CELL RECEPTORS, CARRIERS AND RELATED UNITS

Component	Function	Refs.
Pyridine Nucleotides	Hydrogen transport	–
Hemoglobin	Oxygen and carbon dioxide transport	–
[Lipid] – phosphatidic acid [Lipid] – phosphoinositide	? Na^+ transport ? transport of cell secretions	} 59-61
[Ganglioside]	(Complexes histones) ? Ion transport	} 93, 94, 160, 162
	? Tetanus toxin receptor	147
[Ganglioside] – neuraminic acid	Virus receptor (influenza virus)	11, 44, 71
[Protein or Lipid] – glucose-NH_2	Virus DNA release	11, 74-76
[Protein] – lysine – ε-NH_2	Virus DNA release	74-76
	Pyridoxal phosphate attachment	32
	Amine interaction	17, 122
	? Protein-glutamine amide interaction	17
[Protein] – glutamine amide-NH_2	Amine interaction	17, 99, 100, 102, 122
	?? Insulin receptor	99, 100, 102
	? Ion transport (amidation $\rightleftarrows$ deamidation)	17, 99, 100, 141, 154
[Protein] – cysteine-SH	Antidiuretic hormone receptor	115, 125
	?? Insulin receptor	–
[Protein] – serine-OH	Phosphate attachment (phosphoproteins)	31, 48-50, 113, 157
	? Ion transport	–
[Protein] – Zn^{++} complex	Virus receptor (bacteriophage)	74-76

phate group presumably acting as a "bound" anion with which cations like sodium could complex. A transport scheme quite analogous to that given in Figure 4 has been proposed for this system (60).

Gangliosides have been found by McIlwain (93) to complex with basic histones released from neural cell nuclei on cooling to 0° C., and because of the resultant effects of such complexing on cell excitability and ion fluxes, a possible role of gangliosides in ion transport has been suggested (94, 162). It is of some interest that Wolfe and McIlwain (160) have localized these phenomena to the endoplasmic reticulum of neural cells, a finding which is pertinent to the earlier discussion (cf. Fig. 2) of a possible role for these membranes in solute transfers. It has also been suggested by Van Heyningen (147) that gangliosides may be the receptor sites for tetanus toxin. And as just discussed, the neuraminic acid moiety of gangliosides may be the receptor for certain viruses like the influenza virus (11, 44, 71, 74), and the hexosamine moiety of gangliosides or analogous compounds facilitates release of viral DNA into host cells (11, 75).

A number of protein components may function in comparable fashions. The ϵ-amino group of protein-bound lysine presumably would facilitate release of viral DNA into host cells (75). This same protein moiety appears to be the site of tissue binding of the coenzyme, pyridoxal phosphate (32). There are a number of implications in this observation but its particular relevance here is for the studies by Christensen and co-workers (15, 16, 105) demonstrating enhancement of amino acid uptake into ascites tumor cells by pyridoxal or pyridoxal phosphate. Originally it was thought that this effect might reflect a specific amino acid carrier role for the pyridoxal moiety (15), but subsequent studies have indicated this is a relatively non-specific effect duplicated by other non-pyridoxal compounds (106).

As in other examples to be cited, the attachment of a modifying group to a protein may alter the configuration and/or function of the protein such that transport may be enhanced or modified. Such may be the case for amine interactions and possible protein-bound glutamine amide interactions both with the ϵ-amino group of protein-bound lysine recently reported by Waelsch and associates (17, 122). This same group of investigators has demonstrated more striking interactions between biologically active amines and protein-bound glutamine amide groups (17, 102, 122). The reaction is catalyzed by an enzyme, transglutaminase, present in a variety of mammalian tissues, including brain, and utilizing a number of proteins as substrates, notably insulin (17, 99, 100). Two possibilities are suggested by these studies: one that such reactions may relate to the receptor reaction for insulin (102), and the other that this system may be involved in a cyclic deamidation and reamidation of protein-bound glutamate (100). The studies by Waelsch and his group have demonstrated the deamidation reaction (100), and evidence consistent with the reamidation reaction in cerebral cortex has recently been obtained in our laboratory (141, 154). The potential significance of such a cyclic reaction for ion transport and intracellular fluid balance may be appreciated by the fact that protein-bound glutamic acid represents part of the cellular pool of "fixed" anions. On amidation to glutamine a portion of the fixed anion pool would be subtracted, and conversely deamidation of protein-bound glutamine to glutamic acid would augment the anion pool, hence the possibility for regulation of a portion of the fixed anion pool would exist (141).

Sulfhydryl (SH-) groups, either free or available from disulfide (-S-S-) linkages, of protein-bound cysteine are well-known to be essential for the function of many enzymatic reactions. Recently Rasmussen, Schwartz and co-workers (115, 125) have reported evidence that such groups function as the receptor for the antidiuretic hormone. The effects of such an attachment by disulfide linkages between the SH- groups of the hormone and SH- groups of the receptor protein on alterations of configuration of the latter which might open additional channels for water transfer through membranes have been suggested schematically by these investigators (125). Somewhat analogous schemes for protein carrier mechanisms have been proposed by Goldacre (41) and Danielli (24). Since insulin also contains SH- groups (in disulfide linkages) a comparable mode of hormone-receptor interaction might be envisaged in this case also, although no evidence for such a possibility has been adduced.*

The hydroxyl (OH) groups attached to protein-bound serine offer another possibility, since it is now recognized that it is this moiety on proteins which is phosphorylated, often in readily reversible fashion (31, 49, 113, 157). The same potential role in ion transport could be assumed for such phosphoproteins as discussed above for phospholipids, and it is of interest in this regard that Heald (48, 49) has observed the turnover of brain phosphoprotein phosphate to be very active and has suggested that this active protein fraction is localized in neural cell membranes (50).

Finally there are various metallo-proteins, such as hemoglobin on the one hand and the zinc-protein receptor for bacteriophage virus (75, 76) on the other, which may function in these processes. Again insulin could be considered here, since it is a zinc-containing protein.

Conclusion

Clearly there is a relatively vast amount of information available concerning the mechanisms of transfers of solutes across cell membranes. Much

---

* A recent report by Cadenas *et al.* (*J. Biol. Chem.*, 236: PC 63, 1961) presents evidence for a disulfide (-S-S-) linkage of insulin to heart muscle in a manner quite analogous to that proposed for anti-diuretic hormone binding to receptor proteins.

attention is currently being devoted to neural aspects of this general problem. Such studies have already led to a better appreciation of the blood-brain barrier mechanism as a real entity and to a considerable clarification of its functional role. In addition distinctive features of transport across neural membranes, particularly in the case of amino acids, compared to those for cells in other body tissues, are already apparent. Progress in these areas may be expected to be rapid and fruitful.

Some conception of the nature of receptors and carriers mediating transport has been suggested, but it is obvious much remains to be done in the elucidation of the precise mechanisms and identification of the specific membrane units involved.

Since the body as a whole functions largely in terms of membranes and surface reactions, and since nowhere is this more functionally relevant than in the nervous system, the fundamental importance of these investigations cannot be overestimated. Relationships of membranes and the transport processes occurring across them to dysfunctions of the nervous system have not been discussed in detail, but are implicit in much of the discussion. These are pertinent in the contexts of genetic aberrations, the multitude of agencies which interfere with neural cell energy metabolism, infectious and degenerative diseases and approaches to their therapy, and the developmental and maturational processes of the blood-brain barrier mechanism and neural cells.

In the nervous system, membranes subserve at least two fundamental functions. The surface phenomena associated with excitability and the reception, conduction and transmission of impulses are characteristic and highly developed for neural membranes. And as in most well-differentiated cells, compartmentation of tissue and cellular functions and metabolism by membranes is clearly essential. Both these aspects require the operation of transport processes across the various membranes for supply and for exclusion purposes. The examples cited in this paper of physiological and pathological modifications of membranes and their transport mechanisms underscore the vital nature of these processes. Thus, much of what we take for granted as characteristic of the special behavior, functions and metabolism of neural cells derives from the properties of the membranes and their associated transport processes with which these cells are endowed.

REFERENCES

1. Agar, W. T., Hird, F. J. R., and Sidhu, G. S. *Biochim. Biophys. Acta, 14:* 80 (1954).
2. Agar, W. T., Hird, F. J. R., and Sidhu, G. S. *Biochim. Biophys. Acta, 22:* 21 (1956).
3. Andersen, B., and Ussing, H. H. *Acta physiol. Scand., 39:* 228 (1957).
4. Atkinson, R. M., Parsons, B. J., and Smyth, D. H. *J. Physiol., 135:* 581 (1957).
5. Barany, E., and Sperber, E. *Skand. Arch. Physiol., 81:* 290 (1939).
6. Bering, E. A. *J. Neurosurg., 9:* 275 (1952).
7. Beyer, K. H. *Arch. int. Pharmacodyn. Therap., 98:* 97 (1954).
8. Beyer, K. H., Russo, H. F., Tillson, E. K., Miller, A. K., Verwey, W. F., and Gass, S. R. *Am. J. Physiol., 166:* 625 (1951).
9. Beyer, K. H., Woodward, R., Peters, L., Verwey, W. F., and Mattis, P. A. *Science, 100:* 107 (1944).
10. Bihler, I., and Crane, R. K. *Fed. Proc., 20:* 140 (1961).
11. Bogoch, S. *Neurology, 10:* 439 (1960).
12. Chambers, R., and Zweifach, B. W. *Physiol. Rev., 27:* 436 (1947).
13. Chapman-Andresen, C., and Holter, H. *Exp. Cell Res., Supp. 3:* 52 (1955).
14. Chirigos, M. A., Greengard, P., and Udenfriend, S. *J. Biol. Chem., 235:* 2075 (1960).
15. Christensen, H. N., and Riggs, T. R. *J. Biol. Chem., 220:* 265 (1956).
16. Christensen, H. N., Riggs, T. R., and Coyne, B. A. *J. Biol. Chem., 209:* 413 (1954).
17. Clarke, D. D., Neidle, A., Sarkar, N. K., and Waelsch, H. *Arch. Biochem., 71:* 277 (1957); *79:* 338 (1959).
18. Cohen, G. N., and Monod, J. *Bacteriol. Rev., 21:* 169 (1957).
19. Crane, R. K. *Physiol. Rev., 40:* 789 (1960).
20. Crane, R. K., and Mandelstam, P. *Biochim. Biophys. Acta, 45:* 460 (1960).
21. Crane, R. K., and Sols, A. *J. Biol. Chem., 203:* 273 (1953).
22. Crane, R. K., and Sols, A. *J. Biol. Chem., 210:* 597 (1954).
23. Csáky, T. Z., and Thale, M. *J. Physiol., 151:* 59 (1960).
24. Danielli, J. F. *Sympos. Soc. Exp. Biol., 8:* 502 (1954).
25. Davson, H., and Spaziani, F. *J. Physiol., 149:* 135 (1959).
26. Dobbing, J. *Physiol. Rev., 41:* 130 (1961).
27. Elliott, K. A. C., and Hobbiger, F. *J. Physiol., 146:* 70 (1959).
28. Elliott, K. A. C., and Van Gelder, N. M. *J. Neurochem., 3:* 28 (1958).
29. Farquhar, M. G., and Hartmann, F. G. *J. Neuropath. Exp. Neurol., 16:* 18 (1957).
30. Fick, A. *Ann. Phys. Chem., 94:* 59 (1855).
31. Fischer, E. H., Graves, D. J., Crittenden, E. R. S., and Krebs, E. G. *J. Biol. Chem., 234:* 1698 (1959).
32. Fischer, E. H., Kent, A. B., Snyder, E. R., and Krebs, E. G. *J. Am. Chem. Soc., 80:* 2906 (1958).

33. Fishman, R. A. *Am. J. Physiol., 175:* 96 (1953).
34. Fishman, R. A. *J. Clin. Investig., 38:* 1698 (1959).
35. Frazer, A. C. *Sympos. Soc. Exp. Biol., 8:* 490 (1954).
36. Fridhandler, L., and Quastel, J. H. *Arch. Biochem. Biophys., 56:* 424 (1955).
37. Gale, E. F. *J. Gen. Microbiol., 1:* 53 (1947).
38. Geiger, A. *Physiol. Rev., 38:* 1 (1958).
39. Geiger, A., and Yamasaki, S. *J. Neurochem., 1:* 93 (1956).
40. Gerschenfeld, H. M., Wald, F., Zadunaisky, J. A., and De Robertis, E. D. P. *Neurology, 9:* 412 (1959).
41. Goldacre, R. J. *Internat. Rev. Cytol., 1:* 135 (1952).
42. Goodman, J. R., and Moore, R. E. *J. Bacteriol., 71:* 547 (1956).
43. Goodman, J. R., Moore, R. E., and Baker, R. F. *J. Bacteriol., 72:* 736 (1956).
44. Gottschalk, A. *Physiol. Rev., 37:* 66 (1957).
45. Guroff, G., and Udenfriend, S. *J. Biol. Chem., 235:* 3518 (1960).
46. Guroff, G., and Udenfriend, S. *Biochim. Biophys. Acta, 46:* 386 (1961).
47. Guroff, G., King, W., and Udenfriend, S. *J. Biol. Chem., 236:* 1773 (1961).
48. Heald, P. J. *Biochem. J., 66:* 659 (1957).
49. Heald, P. J. *Biochem. J., 68:* 580 (1958).
50. Heald, P. J. *Biochem. J., 78:* 340 (1961).
51. Heinz, E. *J. Biol. Chem., 211:* 781 (1954).
52. Heinz, E. *J. Biol. Chem., 225:* 305 (1957).
53. Heinz, E., and Mariani, H. A. *J. Biol. Chem., 228:* 97 (1957).
54. Heinz, E., and Walsh, P. M. *J. Biol. Chem., 233:* 1488 (1958).
55. Himwich, H. E., and Nahum, L. H. *Am. J. Physiol., 101:* 446 (1932).
56. Hirsch, J. G., and Cohn, Z. A. *J. Exp. Med., 112:* 1005 (1960).
57. Höber, R. *Physikalische Chemie der Zellen und der Gewebe,* p. 264. Leipzig, 1911.
58. Hofmeister, F. *Die chemische Organisation der Zelle.* F. Vieweg, Braunschweig, 1901.
59. Hokin, L. E., and Hokin, M. R. *J. Biol. Chem., 233:* 805 (1958).
60. Hokin, L. E., and Hokin, M. R. *J. Biol Chem., 234:* 1387 (1959).
61. Hokin, L. E., and Hokin, M. R. *Nature (London), 184:* 1068 (1959).
62. Holland, W. C., and Auditore, G. V. *Am. J. Physiol., 183:* 309 (1955).
63. Holmes, J. H., and Tower, D. B. in *Neurochemistry* (Elliott, K. A. C., Page, I. H., and Quastel, J. H., Eds.), p. 262. Thomas, Springfield, 1955.
64. Horecker, B. L., Thomas, J., and Monod, J. *J. Biol. Chem., 235:* 1580; 1586 (1960).
65. Karnovsky, M. L., Evans, W., and Reibstein, R. *Fed. Proc., 20:* 226 (1961).
66. Kepes, A., *Abstr. IV Internat. Biochem. Congr. (Vienna 1958),* p. 78. Pergamon, London, 1960.
67. Kipnis, D. M., and Cori, C. F. *J. Biol. Chem., 234:* 171 (1959).
68. Kipnis, D. M., Helmreich, E., and Cori, C. F. *J. Biol. Chem., 234:* 165 (1959).

69. Kipnis, D. M., and Noall, M. W. *Biochim. Biophys. Acta, 28:* 226 (1958).
70. Klatzo, I., and Miquel, J. *J. Neuropath. Exp. Neurol., 19:* 475 (1960).
71. Klenk, E., and Lempfrid, H. *Ztschr. physiol. chem., 307:* 278 (1957).
72. Koch, A., in *Medical Physiology and Biophysics* (Ruch, T. C., and Fulton, J. F., Eds.), p. 844. Saunders, Philadelphia, 1960.
73. Koefed-Johnsen, V., and Ussing, H. H. *Acta Physiol. Scand., 28:* 60 (1953).
74. Kozloff, L. M. *Ann. Rev. Biochem., 29:* 475 (1960).
75. Kozloff, L. M., and Lute, M. *J. Biol. Chem., 228:* 529, 537 (1957).
76. Kozloff, L. M., Lute, M., and Henderson, K. *J. Biol. Chem., 228:* 511 (1957).
77. Krahl, M. E. *Perspectives in Biol. and Med., 1:* 69 (1957).
78. Lajtha, A. *J. Neurochem., 2:* 209 (1958).
79. Lajtha, A. *J. Neurochem., 3:* 358 (1959).
80. Lajtha, A. in *Neurochemistry* (Elliott, K. A. C., Page, I. H., and Quastel, J. H., Eds.), 2nd Ed. Thomas, Springfield, in press. *J. Neurochem., 7:* 210 (1961).
81. Lajtha, A., Berl, S., and Waelsch, H. *J. Neurochem., 3:* 322 (1959).
82. Lajtha, A., Furst, S., Gerstein, A., and Waelsch, H. *J. Neurochem., 1:* 289 (1957).
83. LeFevre, P. G. *Sympos. Soc. Exp. Biol., 8:* 118 (1954).
84. LeFevre, P. G. *Fed. Proc., 20:* 139 (1961).
85. Levine, R., Goldstein, M. S., Huddlestun, B., and Klein, S. P. *Am. J. Physiol., 163:* 70 (1950).
86. Li, C-L. *J. Neurophysiol., 22:* 436 (1959).
87. Li, C-L, and McIlwain, H. *J. Physiol., 139:* 178 (1957).
88. Liebig, J., Cited by Lowry, O. H., and Hastings, A. B., in *Problems of Ageing* (Cowdry, E. V., Ed.), 2nd Ed., p. 728. Williams and Wilkins, Baltimore, 1942.
89. Lineweaver, H., and Burke, D. *J. Am. Chem. Soc., 56:* 658 (1934).
90. Lundegårdh, H. *Arkiv f. Botanik (Stockholm), 32:* 12 (1945), Cited by Ussing (143).
91. Luse, S. A., in *Inhibition in the Nervous System and γ-Aminobutyric Acid* (Roberts, E., Ed.), p. 29. Pergamon, London, 1960.
92. Manchester, K. L., and Young, F. G. *Biochem. J., 75:* 487 (1960).
93. McIlwain, H. *Biochem. J., 78:* 24 (1961).
94. McIlwain, H., and Balakrishnan, S. *Biochem. J., 79:* 1 P; *81:* 72 (1961).
95. Michaelis, L., and Menten, M. L. *Biochem. Ztschr., 49:* 339 (1913).
96. Mitchell, P. *J. gen. Microbiol., 9:* 273 (1953).
97. Morgan, H. E., Cadenas, E., Regen, D. M., and Park, C. R. *J. Biol. Chem., 236:* 262 (1961).
98. Morgan, H. E., Henderson, M. J., Regen, D. M., and Park, C. R. *J. Biol. Chem., 236:* 253 (1961).
99. Mycek, M. J., Clarke, D. D., Neidle, A., and Waelsch, H. *Arch. Biochem. Biophys., 84:* 528 (1959).
100. Mycek, M. J., and Waelsch, H. *J. Biol. Chem., 235:* 3513 (1960).
101. Neame, K. D., and Wiseman, G. *J. Physiol., 135:* 442 (1957).

102. Neidle, A., Mycek, M. J., Clarke, D. D., and Waelsch, H. *Arch. Biochem. Biophys.,* 77: 227 (1958).

103. Olson, R. E., and Vester, J. W. *Physiol. Rev.,* 40: 677 (1960).

104. Overton, H. *Arch. ges. Physiol.,* 92: 115 (1902).

105. Oxender, D. L., and Christensen, H. N. *J. Biol. Chem.,* 234: 2321 (1959).

106. Pal, P. R., and Christensen, H. N. *J. Biol. Chem.,* 236: 894 (1961).

107. Pappenheimer, J. R. *Physiol. Rev.,* 33: 387 (1953).

108. Pappenheimer, J. R., Heisey, S. R., and Jordan, E. F. *Am. J. Physiol.,* 200: 1 (1961).

109. Pappius, H. M., and Elliott, K. A. C. *Canad. J. Biochem. Physiol.,* 34: 1007 (1956).

110. Park, C. R., Johnson, L. H., Wright, J. H., and Batsel, H. *Am. J. Physiol.,* 191: 13 (1957).

111. Pomerat, C. M. *Texas Rep. Biol. Med.,* 10: 885 (1952).

112. Post, R. L., Morgan, H. E., and Park, C. R. *J. Biol. Chem.,* 236: 269 (1961).

113. Rabinowitz, M., and Lipmann, F. *J. Biol. Chem.,* 235: 1043 (1960).

114. Rafaelsen, O. J. *J. Neurochem.,* 7: 33, 45, 52 (1961).

115. Rasmussen, H., Schwartz, I. L., Schoessler, M. A., and Hochster, G. *Proc. Nat. Acad. Sci.,* 46: 1278 (1960).

116. Richmond, J. E., and Hastings, A. B. *Am. J. Physiol.,* 199: 814 (1960).

117. Robinson, J. R. *Sympos. Soc. Exp. Biol.,* 8: 42 (1954).

118. Robinson, J. R. *Physiol. Rev.,* 40: 112 (1960).

119. Rosenberg, T. *Sympos. Soc. Biol.,* 8: 27 (1954).

120. Rosenberg, T., and Wilbrandt, W. *Internat. Rev. Cytol.,* 1: 65 (1952).

121. Ruska, H., Edwards, G. A., and Caesar, R. *Experientia,* 14: 117 (1958).

122. Sarkar, N. K., Clarke, D. D., and Waelsch, H. *Biochim. Biophys. Acta,* 25: 451 (1957).

123. Sbarra, A. J., and Karnovsky, M. L. *J. Biol. Chem.,* 234: 1355 (1959).

124. Sbarra, A. J., and Karnovsky, M. L. *J. Biol. Chem.,* 235: 2224 (1960).

125. Schwartz, I. L., Rasmussen, H., Schoessler, M. A., Silver, L., and Fong, C. T. O. *Proc. Nat. Acad. Sci.,* 46: 1288 (1960).

126. Schwerin, P., Bessman, S. P., and Waelsch, H. *J. Biol. Chem.,* 184: 37 (1950).

127. Shanes, A. M. *Pharmacol. Rev.,* 10: 59 (1958).

128. Shannon, J. A., and Fisher, S. *Am. J. Physiol.,* 122: 765 (1938).

129. Shy, G. M., and Tower, D. B. Unpublished data.

130. Siekevitz, P., in *Regulation of Cell Metabolism* (Wolstenholme, G. E. W., and O'Connor, C. M., Eds.), p. 17. Little, Brown, Boston, 1960.

131. Sols, A., and Crane, R. K. *J. Biol. Chem.,* 210: 581 (1954).

132. Stern, J. R., Eggleston, L. V., Hems, R., and Krebs, H. A. *Biochem. J.,* 44: 410 (1949).

133. Sweet, W. H., Selverstone, B., Soloway, S., and Stetten, D. *Surg. Forum, Am. Coll. Surg.,* p. 376. Saunders, Philadelphia, 1951.

134. Takagaki, G., Hirano, S., and Nagata, Y. *J. Neurochem.,* 4: 124 (1959).

135. Tower, D. B. *Ann. Protein Conf. (Rutgers),* 13: 71 (1957).

136. Tower, D. B. *J. Neurochem.,* 3: 185 (1958).

137. Tower, D. B., in *Biochemistry of the Central Nervous System, IV Internat. Biochem. Congr.* (Brücke, F., Ed.), p. 213. Pergamon, London, 1959.

138. Tower, D. B., in *Structure and Function of the Cerebral Cortex* (Tower, D. B., and Schade, J. P., Eds.), p. 411. Elsevier, Amsterdam, 1960.

139. Tower, D. B., in *Handbook of Physiology: Neurophysiology* (Field, J., Magoun, H. W., and Hall, V. E., Eds.) vol. 3, p. 1793. American Physiological Society, Washington, 1960.

140. Tower, D. B., and Peters, E. L. Unpublished data.

141. Tower, D. B., Wherrett, J. R., and McKhann, G. M., in *Regional Neurochemistry* (Kety, S. S., and Elkes, J., Eds.), p. 65. Pergamon, Oxford, 1961.

142. Tsukada, Y., Nagata, Y., and Hirano, S. *Nature (London), 186:* 474 (1960).

143. Ussing, H. H. *Nature (London), 160:* 262 (1947).

144. Ussing, H. H. *Adv. Enzymol., 13:* 21 (1952).

145. Ussing, H. H., in *Metabolic Aspects of Transport across Cell Membranes* (Murphy, Q. R., Ed.), p. 39. U. of Wisconsin, Madison, 1957.

146. Van Harreveld, A., and Schade, J. P., in *Structure and Function of the Cerebral Cortex* (Tower, D. B., and Schade, J. P., Eds.), p. 239. Elsevier, Amsterdam, 1960.

147. Van Heyningen, W. E. *J. Gen. Microbiol., 20:* 310 (1959).

148. Van Slyke, D. D., and Meyer, G. M. *J. Biol. Chem., 16:* 197 (1913-14).

149. Waelsch, H. *Lancet, 257:* 1 (1949).

150. Waelsch, H. *Adv. Protein Chem., 6:* 301 (1951).

151. Waelsch, H., in *Structure and Function of the Cerebral Cortex* (Tower, D. B., and Schade, J. P., Eds.), p. 313. Elsevier, Amsterdam, 1960.

152. Waelsch, H., in *Regional Neurochemistry* (Kety, S. S., and Elkes, J., Eds.), p. 57. Pergamon, Oxford, 1961.

153. Weil-Malherbe, H. *Biochem. Soc. Sympos., 8:* 16 (1952).

154. Wherrett, J. R., and Tower, D. B. Unpublished data.

155. Widdas, W. F. *J. Physiol., 125:* 163 (1954).

156. Wilbrandt, W. *Sympos. Soc. Exp. Biol., 8:* 136 (1954).

157. Williams, J., and Sanger, F. *Biochim. Biophys. Acta, 33:* 294 (1959).

158. Wiseman, G. *J. Physiol., 127:* 414 (1955).

159. Wiseman, G. *J. Physiol., 133:* 626 (1956).

160. Wolfe, L. S., and McIlwain, H. *Biochem. J., 78:* 33 (1961).

161. Woodbury, J. W., in *Medical Physiology and Biophysics* (Ruch, T. C., and Fulton, J. F., Eds.), p. 2. Saunders, Philadelphia, 1960.

162. Woodman, R. J., and McIlwain, H. *Biochem. J., 79:* 1 P; *81:* 79 (1961).

Discussion

Amino Acid Transport in the Brain

ABEL LAJTHA

The theoretical aspects of transport through membranes have been discussed by Dr. Tower in this volume. The present paper is intended to illustrate the principles presented by Dr. Tower with a short discussion of some of the recent experiments (13, 17-19) performed in our laboratory in a continuing study of the mechanism of cerebral amino acid influx and efflux. Each of the three types of experimental approaches tried indicated the participation of a carrier-mediated passage of the amino acids into and out of the brain.

It should be emphasized that, although it is likely that the carriers are components of the membranes, it is not justified to assume at present that they are localized in one or even only a few membranes. It is more reasonable to suppose that the carriers are present in most if not all of the membranes—in those surrounding the whole organ; in cell membranes; and in the particular membranes located within the cells, such as mitochondrial and nuclear membranes and endoplasmic reticulum. All these membranes thus have to be considered as components of the brain-barrier system, although one membrane might be the most influential in the case of a particular substance. We should not consider the brain-barrier system as being exclusively outside the cells of the central nervous system. Some of the membranes through which substances might have to pass in order to enter brain cells are shown schematically in Figure 1.

Results

The exchange of amino acids between plasma and brain. This exchange is rapid (12, 15, 16), although there is an impediment to net increase of the levels of amino acids in the brain when plasma amino acids are

43

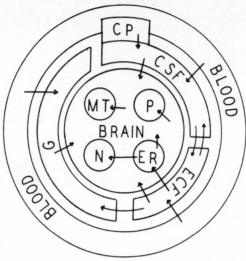

Fɪɢ. 1. Some of the Possible Routes of Passage through Membranes into the Brain. Brain—intracellular space of brain including neuronal and glial elements. CP—choroid plexuses. CSF—cerebrospinal fluid. ECF—extracellular fluid. G—glia. ER—endoplasmic reticulum. MT—mitochondria. N—nuclei. P—other particulate elements (*e.g.*, lysosomes).

elevated. Amino acid exchange can be measured by administering tracer amounts of radioactive amino acids to the plasma without disturbing physiological levels and without inducing net uni-directional transport. In such circumstances, the rate of appearance of a labeled amino acid in the brain (in the case of an amino acid which is not rapidly metabolized) will be indicative of the rate of exchange.

Table 1 shows the relative rate of exchange of lysine and leucine with and without increasing the levels of these amino acids in the brain (17).

Table 1. THE DEPENDENCE OF EXCHANGE RATE ON THE LEVEL OF AMINO ACID IN THE BRAIN

	Relative exchange rate
Leucine exchange at control levels	100
When brain lysine is elevated	100
When brain leucine is elevated	130
Lysine exchange at control levels	100
When brain lysine is elevated	150
When brain leucine is elevated	130

Exchange was measured as the appearance of label in the brain 5 minutes after intravenous administration to rats of C^{14} leucine or C^{14} lysine.

Reference: 17

Table 2. HETEROGENEITY OF LYSINE LEVELS AND LYSINE
EXCHANGE RATES IN VARIOUS BRAIN PARTS

| | L-Lysine | | | | D-Lysine |
| | Normal levels | | Increased levels | | Distribution |
	Distri-bution*	Exchange†	Distri-bution	Exchange	
Cerebellum-Pons-Medulla	150	140	130	130	140
Posterior half of cerebrum	98	99	120	96	120
Anterior half of cerebrum	73	79	69	91	60

*Distribution: μ moles lysine/g fresh tissue, whole brain = 100.

†Exchange: counts/min./g fresh tissue, whole brain = 100.

Brain levels were increased by intracerebral injection of 2 μ moles C^{12} lysine, exchange was measured 5 minutes after intravenous C^{14} lysine injection to rats.

Reference: 17

The rate of exchange at physiological levels is taken as 100. It can be seen that increased leucine levels in the brain resulted in increased leucine exchange whereas increased lysine levels resulted in increased lysine exchange. There was smaller or no effect of leucine on lysine exchange or of lysine on leucine exchange. Thus, when cerebral level was elevated, each of the two amino acids tested increased its own exchange without greatly affecting the rate of exchange of the other amino acid.

The apparent paradox of more label from the blood appearing in the brain though brain levels were elevated (and there was a net efflux from the brain with time) can be explained several different ways; the most likely explanation would seem to be that of carrier-mediated exchange diffusion. It was found in studies of exchange diffusion that an increase of the level of a compound in the cell increased the rate of exchange of that compound (or any other compound transported by the same carrier) between the cell and its medium (6, 7). It would be difficult to explain those results or the results of Table 1 by a passive property of a membrane.

These results show, then, that exchange rates can be altered by changes in cerebral metabolite levels and, at least in the case of the two amino acids discussed, that the exchange rate of one compound can be altered without influencing that of another compound, indicating a metabolite-specific control mechanism in amino acid transport in the brain.

A similar situation (Table 2) exists even when there is no alteration of the physiological levels (13). Lysine under physiological circumstances is not homogeneously distributed in the brain. If exchange is measured, the

Table 3. TRANSPORT OF LEUCINE FROM BRAIN AGAINST
INCREASED PLASMA LEVELS

| | Control | μ moles leucine/100g fresh tissue | | | |
| | | Increase over control | | | |
		20 min.	30 min.	45 min.	60 min.
Plasma	15	210	140	190	230
Brain	11	84	43	18	15
Plasma/Brain		2.5	3.3	11	15

Plasma levels were kept elevated by intravenous and intraperitoneal injec-
tions. In the beginning of the experiment 2 μ moles of the amino acid were
intracerebrally injected to young male rats (average brain weight 1.5g).

Reference: 18

rate will be to some extent proportionate to the lysine content of the area;
that is, physiologically occurring higher lysine levels in an area result in
higher lysine exchange rates. The distribution and exchange in the first two
columns were measured at physiological lysine levels. Similar measurements of distribution and of exchange rates in various brain areas were
performed after elevating the brain lysine level about twofold. The relative
distribution, and consequently the relative exchange rates, were similar
in the brains with physiological and those with elevated levels. The fact
that more of the added amino acid was taken up in those areas which had
a higher level under physiological circumstances indicates, not unexpect-
edly, homeostatic control of amino acid distribution in the brain.

When similar experiments were performed with leucine, it was found
that this amino acid was more homogeneously distributed at physiological
levels than was lysine and that the differences were not very great between
the various brain areas when leucine exchange was measured at control
or at elevated brain leucine levels.

The transport of amino acids from the brain.   Subsequent to the findings
discussed above, a more direct test of active transport was performed: a
test of transport against a concentration gradient in the efflux of amino
acids from the brain. In transport against an increased level, concentration
work (osmotic work, work against a diffusion gradient) is performed;
therefore the process requires energy.

Table 3 presents the results of these tests. In these experiments the
plasma levels of leucine were elevated, and then leucine was intracerebrally administered (for experimental methods and procedures see reference 18). Plasma and brain leucine levels were measured at various times
after leucine administration. The elevated brain leucine levels decreased
with time even though plasma leucine levels were kept well above brain

Table 4. CEREBRAL TRANSPORT OF LYSINE AGAINST
A CONCENTRATION GRADIENT

| | Control | μ moles lysine/100g fresh tissue Increase over control | | | |
		1 hour	2 hours	3 hours	6 hours
Plasma	45	330	340	250	280
Brain	34	84	73	44	50
Plasma/Brain		3.9	4.7	5.7	5.6

For experimental details see Table 3.

Reference: 18

levels throughout the experiment, showing amino acid efflux against a concentration gradient. In a separate set of experiments (19), the amino acids decreased with time in the spinal fluid (CSF) as well, finally leaving the central nervous system through the circulating plasma; however, it has not yet been established if the active transport occurs between brain and blood, brain and CSF, or CSF and blood. After a time the plasma-to-brain ratio of leucine concentration reached a fairly constant value of about 13. This ratio was reached at two different plasma leucine levels and also without prior intracerebral leucine administration. Such an apparent independence of the value of this ratio on the absolute plasma leucine levels or on the route of administration of the amino acid would show that the ratio is a measure of the efficiency of the cerebral "leucine pump."

When the above experiments were repeated using lysine as the test amino acid, the results were similar in that lysine was also transported out of the brain against a concentration gradient of elevated plasma levels. The plasma to brain concentration ratio after a time approached 5.6 (Table 4). Under similar conditions with phenylalanine no transport from the brain against a concentration gradient was shown, since cerebral phenylalanine levels did not decrease with time. The experimental conditions have not been varied widely enough to decide whether active transport of phenylalanine out of the brain occurs at a much lower rate than that of the other amino acids tested or is altogether absent.

Changes in transport in development. In a set of experiments without intracerebral administrations the transport of leucine from the brain against a concentration gradient of elevated plasma levels was compared in adults and newborn. Adult brain levels decreased with time when plasma levels were kept well above brain levels; in newborn the brain levels increased under similar circumstances (Fig. 2). Such findings show

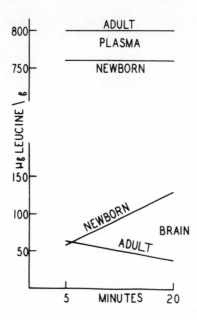

F<small>IG</small>. 2.   Changes in leucine levels with time following intracerebral leucine administrations in newborn and adult brains when plasma leucine levels are elevated.

that at least some of the differences of permeability between adult and newborn can be explained by the further development of transport processes.

Efflux of amino acids from the brain.   The third approach to the investigation of transport processes of cerebral amino acids was a study of the rate of efflux of these compounds from the brain after their intracerebral administration.

The efflux of L-amino acids is shown in Table 5. It can be seen that maximal concentration is reached at different times with the different amino acids and that the time needed for return to physiological levels also varies from one amino acid to another. Experiments similar to the ones described in Table 5 were performed with the D isomers (Table 6). Efflux of the D-amino acids paralleled that of the L-amino acids in that the rate of efflux varied from one amino acid to another and also that the rate of decrease was in decreasing order leucine > phenylalanine > lysine. From the changes in concentrations with time the rate of decrease between the measured time intervals can be calculated; the rates are expressed (Table 7) as the time in minutes required for the level to decrease to half. When efflux rates of the L and D isomers of the amino acids are compared, it can be seen that the difference is the greatest in the case of

Table 5. LEVELS OF L-AMINO ACIDS IN THE BRAIN FOLLOWING THEIR INTRACEREBRAL ADMINISTRATION

Time in minutes	Increase over control μ moles/100g fresh brain			
	Leucine	Proline	Phenylalanine	Lysine
5	40	77	93	33
20	15	100	93	71
45	2.3	37	30	72
60	2.3	22	20	69
120	0	0	5.2	54
180			0	39

2 μ moles of the amino acid were injected intracerebrally in the beginning of the experiments in young (90-100g) male rats.

Reference: 19

Table 6. D-AMINO ACID LEVELS IN RAT BRAIN FOLLOWING INTRACEREBRAL ADMINISTRATION

Time in minutes	μ moles/100g fresh brain		
	Leucine	Phenylalanine	Lysine
1	45	56	
2		77	55
5	59	71	66
20	47	59	84
45	18	38	78
60	12	26	74
120	1.6	4.9	63
180	0.7		49
240			43

2 μ moles of the amino acid were injected intracerebrally in the beginning of the experiments in young (90-100g) male rats.

Reference: 19

Table 7. RELATIVE EFFLUX RATES OF L- AND D-AMINO ACIDS FROM RAT BRAIN

Time intervals in minutes	Minutes for 50% decrease in level*					
	Leucine		Phenylalanine		Lysine	
	L	D	L	D	L	D
5 - 45	14	28				
20 - 120			27	32		
45 - 240					140	200

* $\dfrac{\text{Time interval in minutes}}{\text{\% loss during interval}} \times 50$

Reference: 19

leucine, smaller in the case of lysine, and not significant with phenyla-lanine. These findings are perhaps related to those made in studying the transport of these compounds against a concentration gradient, where the brain levels as compared to plasma levels were lower with leucine than with lysine and no transport of phenylalanine could be shown. In other terms, where a stronger transport out of the brain is present, there is a larger relative difference between the L and D form of the amino acid, showing the stereospecificity of the transport process.

Discussion

It has been known for some time that brain slices can take up amino acids from the incubation medium against a concentration gradient. This observation was made with most of the amino acids studied, including L glutamic acid (23), D glutamic acid (24), γ aminobutyric acid (3, 25), and histidine, proline, lysine, ornithine, methionine, and arginine (20). Inhibition of the production or utilization of energy decreased this uptake against a concentration gradient with glutamic acid (23), aspartic acid (11), gamma aminobutyric acid (3, 25), 5-hydroxytryptophan (22), histidine (20), and tyrosine (4). These studies clearly established the presence of active processes in the transport of amino acids in brain slices.

There can be no doubt that the permeability of the whole brain differs greatly from that of brain slices. However, the above results observed at various times and in a number of laboratories show clearly that some of the transport mechanisms which contribute to the permeability character-istics of the whole brain are present in isolated systems also. This makes a closer study of these processes possible without the interference or super-imposition of at least some of the secondary factors present in the living animal.

Although active transport in brain slices has been known for some time, evidence for the presence of mediated transport in the central nervous system *in vivo* was only recently obtained (1, 13, 14, 21). Active transport of Diodrast and phenolsulfonphthalein from CSF to blood (21) was shown. There was transfer during ventriculocisternal perfusion from CSF into blood even when levels in blood were more than twice that of CSF. The transfer rate of Diodrast per unit concentration difference was over 15-fold greater in the direction CSF to blood than in the reverse direction (the transfer rates of fructose and creatinine were the same in the two directions). The fourth ventricle was proposed as the site of active transport. Inhibition of the active component of transport revealed the passive component: diffusion and absorption by bulk (21). In a study of cerebral tyrosine uptake (1) it was found that the penetration of this amino acid into brain was inhibited by some but not all of the other amino acids, indicating more than one specific site for cerebral amino acid entry. The penetration of L-tyrosine was more rapid than that of its D isomer.

In a recent study of the penetration of tyrosine in slices and in whole brain it was found that the diffusion component present in slices was absent *in vivo* and that the *in vivo* transport was stereospecific although the cellular transport measured in slices was not. Comparing tyrosine transport in brain slices with that of kidney, liver, or spleen slices and diaphragm, energy-dependent concentrative uptake was found in brain slices only (4, 5). Concentrative uptake of gamma aminobutyrate was another property of brain slices which could not be shown with kidney or liver slices or diaphragm (3, 25). It should be recalled in this regard that active transport of glutamic acid (23) was not specific for brain slices, but was present in kidney cortex, spleen, lung and chorion *in vitro*.

Increased exchange when brain levels are elevated does not necessarily require active transport, but it obviously cannot be explained by passive diffusion through a membrane. Among the several possible mechanisms, that of exchange diffusion is the most likely. This has been studied in detail mostly using glycine and Ehrlich ascites carcinoma cells; a schematic model for this mechanism has been proposed (2, 8, 10). Preloading the cells with glycine increased the influx coefficient of this amino acid without changing the efflux coefficient, and this was interpreted as being due to an increased rate of glycine exchange diffusion across the osmotic barrier of the cell (8). The results with ascites cells suggest that exchange diffusion and active transport of glycine refer to the same mechanism (8, 10).

It is tempting to think that at least a part of the mechanism of amino acid transport in the brain is similar to the one in Ehrlich ascites cells. Whatever the mechanism is, however, the increase by lysine or leucine of its own exchange rate (Tables 1, 2) shows that some of the processes in amino acid transport are not constant but can be altered by changes in the composition of metabolites in the brain, and that such effects can be specific, that is, the exchange rate of one compound can be changed without affecting that of another compound. Such changes can be specific in another sense—some alteration might occur in one specific brain area without affecting other areas.

The finding of transport from the brain against a concentration gradient (Tables 3, 4) is more direct evidence for active transport, in this case, in the direction from brain to blood. This finding shows that metabolite levels can be regulated not only by the control of influx into the brain but also by control of efflux. Comparison of the behavior of the amino acids studied up to the present time does not permit us to decide if the influx and efflux of any amino acid occurs through the same mechanism or if flux in the two directions is individually controlled (by different mechanisms). In galactose transport in *E. Coli* the exit process was found to be independent, at least to some extent, of the entry process (9). Transport processes in either direction may require energy.

That phenylalanine transport cannot be found under the same experimental conditions in which leucine and lysine transport against a concentration gradient of increased plasma level occurs does not necessarily mean that no active transport of phenylalanine exists. It is possible that the amino acid "pumps" of the brain work with varying degrees of efficiency and that at lower plasma to brain concentration gradient phenylalanine transport does occur. An alternate explanation would be that the tissue has a greater capacity for uptake or has a higher tolerance to phenylalanine before active transport is initiated. That the barrier system is not entirely absent for phenylalanine is shown by the fact that the uptake of this amino acid from blood by the brain when plasma levels are elevated is restricted as compared to tissues such as liver or muscle (18).

The results of studies of efflux of the amino acids when plasma levels are not elevated (Tables 5, 6) parallel the studies of transport against a gradient. The differences between the L and D isomers show stereospecificity of the transport process, but such differences do not necessarily mean active transport (5).

It is important to establish the differences between brain and other tissues. There is no doubt that the permeability properties of the brain differ quantitatively from those of most other tissues, but it has not been definitely shown if any mechanisms exist in the brain that are not operative in other tissues. Previously mentioned studies (3-5, 25) give indications that some of the active cellular transport processes may be specific for brain.

Summary

The membranes of the central nervous system appear at closer examination—at least as far as the amino acids, and possibly most physiologically occurring metabolites, are concerned—to be not just semipermeable membranes involving only passive diffusion, but, rather, to be sites of numerous transport mechanisms. In this sense the brain-barrier system becomes a homeostatic and metabolic control mechanism, possessing more properties than a passive membrane, which could not alter flux rates of specific substances. It will perhaps emerge that specific substrates can be transported into an area when and where needed and that the influx or efflux of substrates and their metabolic products can be altered without affecting all other metabolites in that particular area.

The results discussed in the present paper furnish indications rather than definite conclusions about this complex system but the following properties have been indicated:

a. Control (the rate of entry and exit, as well as cerebral levels).

b. Metabolite specificity (alterations in flux or level of a few or of a single metabolite).

c. Metabolite variability (differences in efficiency or tolerance towards various compounds).

d. Regional variability (local differences, with the possibility of specific changes in one particular area).

e. Stereospecificity.

f. Active component (net transport against a diffusion gradient).

g. Two-directional transport (active component and perhaps most other characteristics, such as control affecting efflux as well as influx).

h. Development (changes during development in active as well as passive transport components).

At present more questions are raised than answered. Some of the questions that cannot be answered are the following: Does exchange occur through an energy requiring process? Is there a single carrier or are there multiple carriers mediating exchange, influx, and efflux? Are there separate carriers for each substrate? What are the kinetics of the transport processes? Which metabolic reactions supply energy? Which processes are specific for the nervous system? There are many more. Future research will no doubt simplify as well as clarify our picture of transport mechanisms in the central nervous system, answer our questions about the role of these mechanisms in health and disease, and with understanding give us the possibility of influencing these processes.

REFERENCES

1. Chirigos, M., Greengard, P., and Udenfriend, S. *J. Biol. Chem.*, 235: 2075 (1960).
2. Christensen, H. N. *Adv. Prot. Chem.*, 15: 239 (1960).
3. Elliott, K. A. C., and Van Gelder, N. M. *J. Neurochem.*, 3: 28 (1958).
4. Guroff, G., King, W., and Udenfriend, S. *J. Biol. Chem.*, 236: 1773 (1961).
5. Guroff, G., and Udenfriend, S. *J. Biol. Chem.*, 235: 3518 (1960).
6. Heinz, E. *J. Biol. Chem.*, 211: 781 (1954).
7. Heinz, E., and Durbin, R. P. *J. Gen. Physiol.*, 41: 101 (1957).

8. Heinz, E., and Walsh, P. M. *J. Biol. Chem.,* 233: 1488 (1958).
9. Horecker, B. L., Thomas, J., and Monod, J. *J. Biol. Chem.,* 235: 1586 (1960).
10. Johnstone, R. M., and Quastel, J. H. *Biochem. Biophys. Acta,* 46: 527 (1961).
11. Korey, S. R., and Mitchell, R. *Biochem. Biophys. Acta,* 7: 507 (1951).
12. Lajtha, A. *J. Neurochem.,* 3: 358 (1959).
13. Lajtha, A., in *Regional Neurochemistry* (Kety, S. S., and Elkes, J., Eds.), p. 19. Pergamon Press, Oxford, 1961.
14. Lajtha, A., in *Neurochemistry* (Elliott, K. A. C., Page, I., and Quastel, J. K., Eds.). C. C. Thomas, Springfield, in press.
15. Lajtha, A., Berl, S., and Waelsch, H. *J. Neurochem.,* 3: 322 (1959).
16. Lajtha, A., Furst, S., Gerstein, A., and Waelsch, H. *J. Neurochem.,* 1: 289 (1957).
17. Lajtha, A., and Mela, P. *J. Neurochem.,* 7: 210 (1961).
18. Lajtha, A., and Toth, J. *J. Neurochem.,* 8 (1961).
19. Lajtha, A., and Toth, J. *J. Neurochem.,* in press.
20. Neame, K. D. *J. Neurochem.,* 6: 358 (1961).
21. Pappenheimer, J. R., Heisey, S. R., and Jordan, E. F. *Am. J. Physiol.,* 200: 1 (1961).
22. Schanberg, S., and Giarman, N. J. *Biochem. Biophys. Acta,* 41: 556 (1960).
23. Stern, J. R., Eggleston, L. V., Hems, R., and Krebs, H. A. *Biochem. J.,* 44: 410 (1949).
24. Takagaki, G., Hirano, S., and Nagata, Y. *J. Neurochem.,* 4: 124 (1959).
25. Tsukada, Y., Nagata, Y., and Hirano, S. *Nature,* 186: 474 (1960).

Membrane and Myelin

SARAH A. LUSE

Electron microscopy has radically altered our concepts of the structure of the myelin sheath. No longer is it considered as merely a lipid sheath enclosing the axon, but rather is now known to be an intricate lamellar structure that is a part of the sheath cell. Electron microscopy also has created new problems in both terminology and ideology. One of these is evident in the current philosophy that all axons are myelinated. Since myelin is a lamellated membranous structure, and since all axons have at least a single cell membrane about them, it is therefore reasoned that all axons are medullated, thus making a farce of the term *myelin* rather than leading to a correlation of structure and function. Still other problems remain unsolved. In spite of new information concerning fine structure of myelin, the stimulus or signal for myelin formation is yet unknown— whether it be a response to conduction in the axon, a response to some "neurohumor" produced by the axon, or a product of the glial or satellite cell. Thus the stimulus that incites the sheath cell to produce myelin membranes is as much an unanswered question as is the signal that halts myelin production. Another enigma concerns the "C" fibers with their multiple axons within a single Schwann cell, rather than the single axon within a Schwann cell of the myelinated axon. Does the fundamental difference between an unmyelinated and a myelinated axon, then, reside in the sheath cell or in the axon?

Equally current is the question as to the source of the membrane that forms the myelin sheath. Gasser (3) demonstrated that multiple unmyelinated axons were enclosed in the cytoplasm of a Schwann cell and that a mesaxon of Schwann plasma membrane connected the axons to the

This work was supported in part by Grants B1539 and B425 from the National Institutes of Health, Bethesda, Maryland.

55

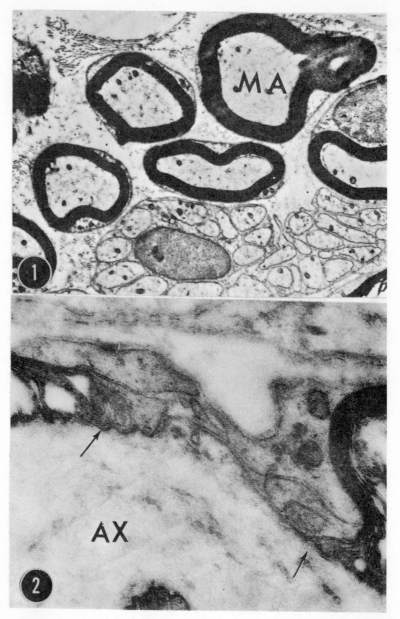

Fig. 1. Cross-section of normal adult sciatic nerve (rabbit). Parts of 6 myelinated axons are present (MA). The Schwann cytoplasm about them is scant and contains few organelles. At the bottom of the figure is part of a Schwann cell containing numerous unmyelinated "C" fibers. (× *approximately 4,000*)

Fig. 2. Part of a peripheral node of Ranvier. The axoplasm (AX) is at the lower part of the figure. The myelin sheath ends (arrows) at each side of the nodal region which is covered by Schwann cytoplasm and a basement membrane. (× *12,000*)

surface of the sheath cell. Geren (4) showed that the myelinated axon also is enclosed by a Schwann cell, but that there is only a single axon per Schwann cell, and that the myelin sheath is continuous with the plasma membrane of the Schwann cell. She hypothesized that myelin is formed by a rotation of the Schwann cell, whereas Luse (7) and de Robertis, Gerschenfeld and Wald (2) have suggested, as has Hodge (5), that myelin is formed by fusion of cytoplasmic vesicles. This does not necessarily imply that this membrane, formed from fused vesicular structures, is not incorporated into the plasma membrane of the Schwann cell prior to incorporation into the myelin sheath. But it does imply a meta-bolically-active Schwann cell, and such is the case, suggesting a mechanism whereby the cell might manufacture the large amount of membrane necessary to form myelin.

If one examines a mature myelinated peripheral axon, one notes that the Schwann cytoplasm is scant and contains few organelles (Fig. 1). Near the node the cytoplasm may become more abundant (Fig. 2) and often contains vesicles. Myelin lamellae are arranged in a uniformly repeating pattern with an indistinct interzone line (Fig. 3). In contrast to these mature Schwann cells is their appearance at the time of active myelin formation. At this period it is an active metabolic machine containing numerous mitochondria, abundant ergastoplasm and numerous smooth-outlined vesicular forms (Fig. 4). The important and not yet definitively answered questions are: How does the Schwann cell make membrane? How does this membrane become organized into myelin? What are the stimuli that initiate and end myelinization?

It is important to consider myelin formation in the central nervous system as well as in peripheral nerve. In the central nervous system nodes of Ranvier also occur (Fig. 5), pointing to similarity in structural organization. However, in the closely packed neuropil it is impossible to trace a single axon for a long distance, or to follow processes of glial cells with certainty. Thus, we cannot say definitively that a single internodal length of axon is related to a single oligodendrocyte. In fact, it may well be that more than one glial cell contributes to the myelin sheath of a single segment of myelin. The first sign of myelination in the central nervous system occurs as a series of "spot welds" or desmosomes. Then, as glial processes insert themselves between the unmyelinated axons there is a predominance of oligodendroglial processes containing numerous vesicles. This has suggested to de Robertis *et al.* (2) and to Luse (7) that membrane is being formed from these vesicles (Fig. 6). In addition there is evidence in the central nervous system that some myelin results from overlapping of glial processes (6) (Fig. 7). The myelinated sheath in a mature brain is seen in Figure 8.

A third type of myelin, different from both that of the peripheral and

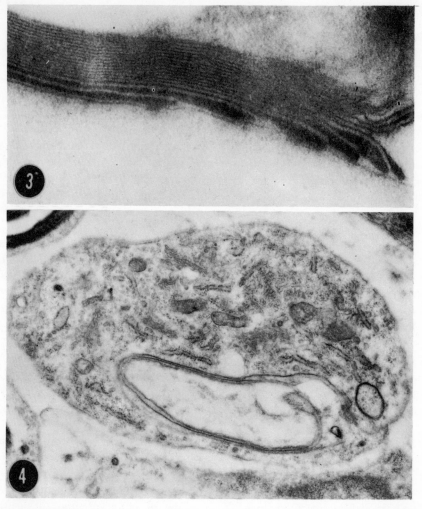

FIG. 3. Mature peripheral myelin sheath from near a node of Ranvier (to the right of the figure). The innermost lamellae end farthest from the node. (× *approximately 80,000*)

FIG. 4. Myelinating axon in sciatic nerve of a new-born animal. The Schwann cell has abundant cytoplasm filled with mitochondria, ergastoplasm and numerous vesicular structures. (× *approximately 8,000*)

FIG. 5. Node of Ranvier in brain of adult mouse. A single large mitochondrion is present in the nodal region. (× *7,500*)

FIG. 6. A central nervous system axon that is just beginning to myelinate. Numerous vesicles (arrows) are present at the margin of the axon. (× *12,000*)

FIG. 7. Two axons in the brain of a 5-day-old mouse. Surrounding them are irregular lamellae of developing myelin. There are multiple regions where the dense myelin membranes continue into the plasma membranes of glial processes. Some of these are marked with arrows. (× *12,000*)

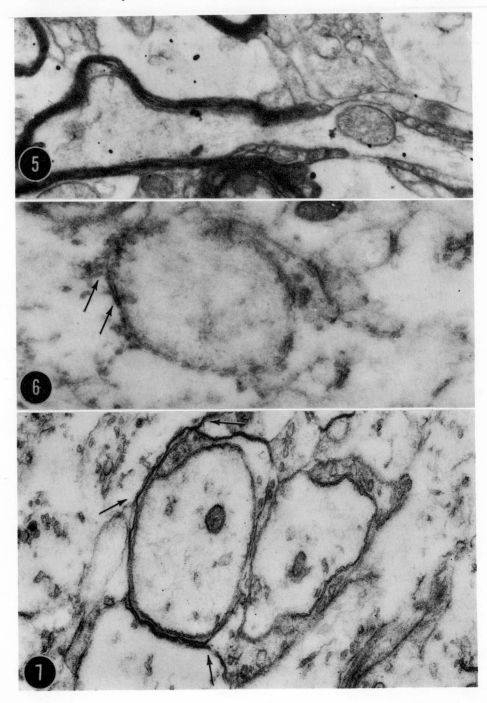

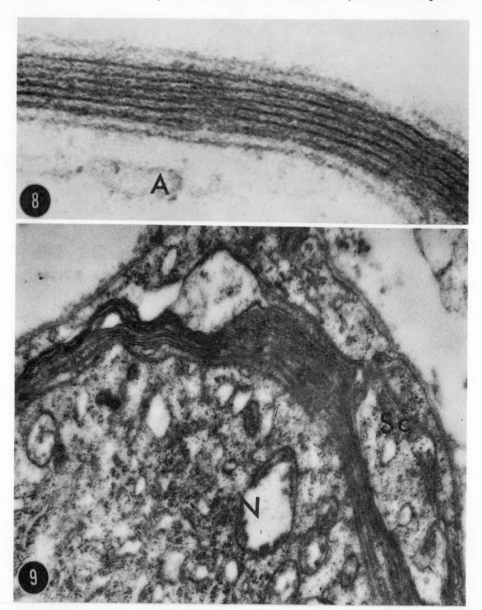

FIG. 8.   High magnification of myelin sheath in the brain of an adult rabbit. The axon (A) is at the bottom of the field. (× *approximately 280,000*)

FIG. 9.   This is a myelinated neuron (N) in the vestibular ganglion of an adult rabbit. The multilamellar myelin sheath closely invests the neuron and external to it is the satellite cell cytoplasm (Sc). (× *15,000*)

the central axon, occurs about the nerve cell bodies of both the vestibular and cochlear ganglia (Fig. 9). Nodes occur in this myelin sheath. Multiple sheath or satellite cells are involved in the formation of these large areas of organized lamellar myelin. Rotation of the satellite cells about these neurons would lead to a different type of myelin without nodes. In addition the nucleus and cell body cannot surround the entire neuron being myelinated, but rather are superficial to the myelin of part of the neuron, suggesting that myelin is laid down in an area that is within the zone of influence of a single sheath cell.

Perhaps, then, more than one mechanism may act in the formation of any myelin sheath. I would like to urge, as Dr. Tower has suggested, that we should not separate the nervous system from other organ systems. To do so isolates the brain, whereas it actually is a part of the total biology, and related to the phenomena occurring elsewhere in nature. In particular, I would like to point out that organized multilamellar systems are common to many areas: the chloroplasts of plants, myelin figures in cells where lipoprotein building blocks are available, myelin sheaths, retinal rods, and *in vitro* in myelin figures (9) formed from phospholipid and water. It is not my purpose to propose that these lamellar structures are myelin, but rather that they represent similar biologic phenomena.

Having demonstrated the three types of myelin sheaths, I would now like to proceed to the methods by which these sheaths can be destroyed. As was mentioned earlier, it is necessary to have both a neurite and a sheath cell before myelin will form. Similarly, the integrity of both the axon and the sheath cell is necessary for the maintenance of the myelin sheath. Thus, demyelination will result from an insult to either the neuron or its axon, or to the sheath cell.

Wallerian degeneration is a prototype of demyelination occurring following an insult to either the neuron or its axon. The axon undergoes disintegration and only later does the myelin sheath break up. Peripherally, this is a rapid process with most of the lipid debris removed within 40 days (Fig. 10). Hyperplasia of Schwann cells occurs to form the tubes of Büngner, and the early disintegration of the myelin occurs within the Schwann cytoplasm. In the central nervous system removal of lipid debris is greatly slowed by the fibrous astrocytic gliotic response. Even at 100 to 200 days large amounts of myelin breakdown products are still present.

Some of the spontaneously occurring demyelinating diseases of the nervous system present changes similar to those in Wallerian degeneration. One of these is the hereditary ataxia of rabbits (1). In this disease there is demyelination and degeneration in the vestibular and cochlear nuclei and tracts. By electron microscopy it is evident that the first changes are within the axons (Fig. 11). Mitochondria and axoplasm swell, and only later does the myelin sheath (Fig. 12) undergo dissolution.

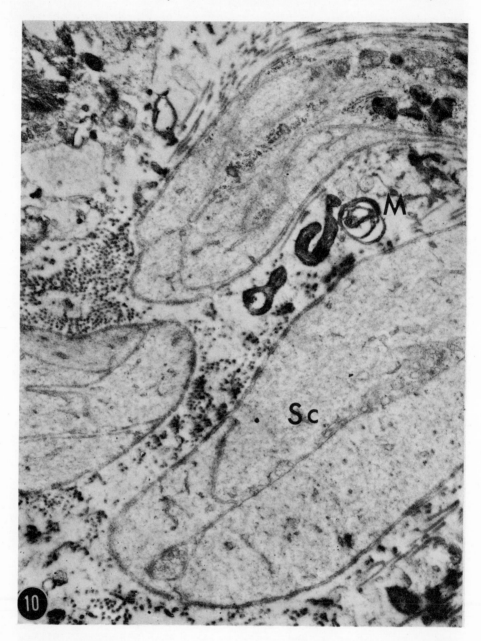

FIG. 10. Wallerian degeneration. This sciatic nerve had been cut 45 days previously. In the distal segment axons and most myelin debris were absent. Myelin debris is evident (M). Most of the nerve is composed of hypertrophied Schwann cytoplasm (Sc). Collagen fibers are prominent. (× 15,000)

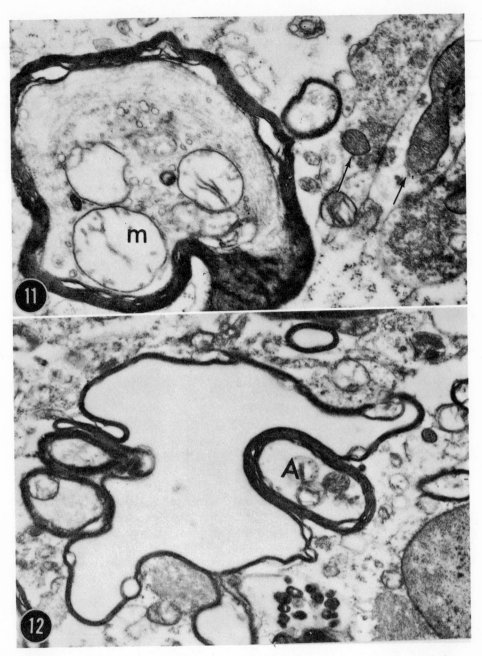

FIG. 11.   Early Wallerian degeneration in the CNS. This is an axon in the vestibular nucleus of the medulla of an ataxic rabbit. The mitochondria (m) in the axoplasm are severely swollen whereas mitochondria in adjacent structures (arrows) are normal. The myelin is still intact. (× 15,000)

FIG. 12.   A later stage of degeneration in the ataxic rabbit medulla. The axon (A) is virtually destroyed and the myelin is beginning to disintegrate. (× 8,000)

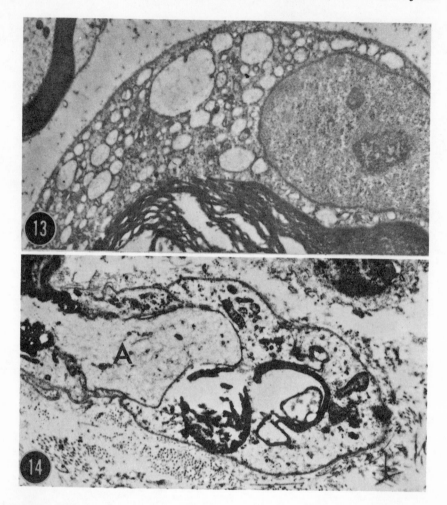

FIG. 13.   Experimental allergic encephalomyelitis. This is an early stage in the changes in the peripheral nerve root. The Schwann cell cytoplasm is increased in amount and its organelles are swollen. Myelin is not yet destroyed. (× 8,000)

FIG. 14.   A later stage in the changes in a peripheral nerve fiber in experimental allergic encephalomyelitis. The axon (A) is preserved. The myelin sheath is destroyed. Myelin debris is present in the hypertrophied Schwann cell cytoplasm. (× 8,000)

FIG. 15.   Experimental allergic encephalomyelitis. In the spinal cord numerous de-myelinated axons (A) are present at this late stage. (× 12,000)

FIG. 16.   Tuberculoma of the spinal cord in a human being. A lymphocyte is present at the lower left. Many axons (A) were preserved but were without myelin and were surrounded by some type of glial or sheath cell. (× 8,000)

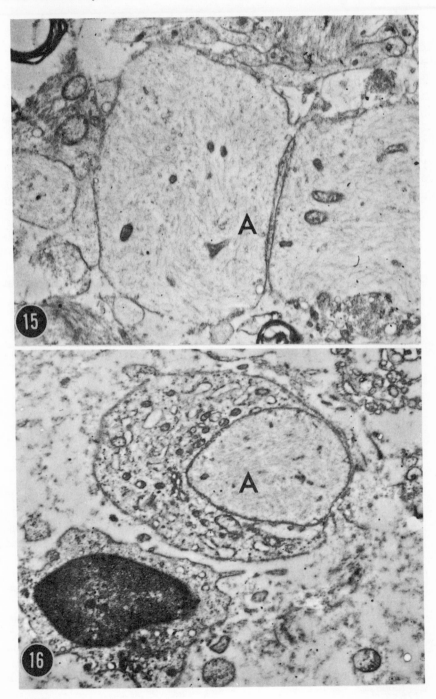

The second major type of demyelination is the result of an insult to the sheath cell, be it Schwann cell or oligodendrocyte. The prototype of this lesion, truly a demyelination, is seen in experimental allergic encephalomyelitis (8). The first changes seen are swelling of the cytoplasm and of the cellular organelles in the sheath cells, as in a Schwann cell in Figure 13. Similar changes occur in the oligodendrocytes. Later, the myelin disintegrates (Fig. 14) but the axon is unaltered. In the central nervous system multiple demyelinated axons then are evident (Fig. 15).

In a spontaneously occurring tuberculoma of the spinal cord a similar type of demyelination was observed (Fig. 16). Axons were spared but the myelin sheaths were destroyed. From light microscopic studies one is justified in predicting that a similar picture will probably be seen in multiple sclerosis.

In summary, I would like to point out again the close morphologic relationship that exists between the multilaminated structures in many biologic systems. Our knowledge of the structure, function, and maintenance of myelin will be amplified if we attempt to understand the processes as they involve all myelinated axons, *in vivo* and *in vitro*.

REFERENCES

1. Anders, M. V.: The histopathology of a new type of hereditary loss of coordination in the domestic rabbit. *Am. J. Anat., 76:* 183-194 (1945).
2. De Robertis, E., Gerschenfeld, H. M., and Wald, F.: Cellular mechanism of myelination in the central nervous system. *J. Biophysic. and Biochem. Cytol., 4:* 651-658 (1958).
3. Gasser, H. S.: Properties of dorsal root unmedullated fibers on the two sides of the ganglion. *J. Gen. Physiol., 38:* 709-728 (1955).
4. Geren, B. B.: The formation from the Schwann cell surface of myelin in the peripheral nerves of chick embryos. *Exper. Cell Res., 7:* 558-562 (1954).
5. Hodge, A. J.: Effects of the physical environment on some lipoprotein layer systems and observations on their morphogenesis. *J. Biophysic. and Biochem. Cytol., 2:* 221-227 (1956).
6. Luse, S. A.: Formation of myelin in the central nervous system of mice and rats, as studied with the electron microscope. *J. Biophysic. and Biochem. Cytol., 2:* 777-784 (1956).
7. Luse, S. A.: The fine structure of the morphogenesis of myelin. *Progr. Neurobiol., 4:* 59-81 (1959).
8. Luse, S. A., and McDougal, D. B.: Electron microscopic observations on allergic encephalomyelitis in the rabbit. *J. Exp. Med., 112:* 735-742 (1960).
9. Stoeckenium, W.: An electron microscope study of myelin figures. *J. Biophysic. and Biochem. Cytol., 5:* 491-500 (1959).

Discussion

MURRAY B. BORNSTEIN

A valuable trait of Dr. Luse's work is revealed in her presentation: her ability to raise reasonable doubts both in areas of recent development as well as in those more studied fields where doubt was not generally thought to exist.

One such controversy, introduced some years ago by Dr. Luse (6), continues to interest investigators concerned with the mode of myelin formation in the central nervous system. Dr. Luse concluded that the multi-layered structure might be produced, in part, by the cell membranes of a single neuroglial process wrapping around the axon, similar in action to the formation of peripheral myelin by the Schwann cell. This thesis agrees with that of most other workers involved in the problem of central myelination. The idea, however, appeared inadequate to explain all the observed facts. Dr. Luse, therefore, further suggested that another mechanism might also exist, namely that multiple neuroglial processes might contribute their membranes to the layering of myelin about any particular portion of axon.

While Dr. Luse was observing the ultrastructural details of *in vivo* myelination in the central nervous system of rats and mice, we were involved with the living events of myelin formation as visualized directly by serial observations of cultured newborn kitten and rat cerebellum (4). We suggested that a multiple neuroglial mechanism could explain the *in vitro* course of events, *i.e.*, the abrupt, simultaneous appearance of myelin

These data originated from studies conducted in the Laboratory of Cellular Neurophysiology, The Mount Sinai Hospital; the Laboratory for Cell Physiology and the Division of Neuropathology, Columbia University, College of Physicians and Surgeons; and the Department of Anatomy, Cornell University, Medical College, New York.

The work was supported by grants No. B-1913, B-858, 2B-5062 and B-1523 from the U.S.P.H.S. and grant No. 246 from the National Multiple Sclerosis Society.

extending over 1 to 2 mm.-long segments of axon with no apparent break in the continuity of the sheath. We were gratified, therefore, to learn that Dr. Luse had proposed a similar idea based on electron microscopic observations. Since then, Dr. Leonard Ross has examined the details of *in vitro* myelination as revealed by the electron microscope (7). Significant stages during myelination, as determined by direct observation of the cultured fragment, were instantaneously stopped by fixation. The tissues were then embedded and sectioned for ultrastructural study.

Dr. Ross' electron micrographs of tissue fixed just prior to myelin formation reveal axons against which a number of neuroglial cells lie separated by about 200 Å, the distance usually found between cell membranes of an epithelial structure. It would be interesting to speculate about the mechanisms involved in the reduction of this distance which must occur during the formation of the myelin sheath.

During the phase of early myelin formation, usually about the tenth to the fourteenth day *in vitro*, single neuroglial cell processes may be seen spiralling around the axon. The internal mesaxon and, occasionally, an external lip are observed. Other axons, however, appear to be involved with multiple neuroglial cell processes, each seemingly contributing to the multiple layering. In later stages, when the myelin is becoming compact, it becomes almost impossible to visualize with certainty what has happened between the various closely spaced layers of membrane.

A fortunate occurrence permitted observations of the internal lamellar arrangements during these later stages of myelin formation. In another study, 18-day-old cultures were exposed to sera withdrawn from rabbits with experimental "allergic" encephalomyelitis (2). The earliest action of these sera causes a swelling of neuroglia which, in turn, tends to push their cytoplasm back between the cell membranes wrapped around the axon. The resultant "exploded diagram" of the later stages of myelin formation reveals the relationships between lamellae. It was then evident that the internal structure might be produced by multiple neuroglial cell processes interdigitating about any particular portion of axon.

From the observations of cultured material, we must agree with Dr. Luse that, although one neuroglial cell process may spiral once, twice or even three times about an axon, this is not the only mechanism, and that multiple processes may also contribute to the final multi-lamellated structure of the adult myelin sheath in the central nervous system.

The second part of this discussion is related to the cell membranes and the myelin sheath during a process of *in vitro* demyelination.

As was mentioned above (2), Dr. Stanley Appel and I have exposed cultures of rat cerebellum to the sera of rabbits with experimental "allergic" encephalomyelitis (EAE). These sera produce a characteristic and specific demyelination *in vitro* strikingly similar to that which occurs in the animal—the rapid destruction of myelin with relative preservation of neurons and axis cylinders. In fact, the cultures remyelinate when returned to normal *in vitro* conditions (3).

A significant problem arising from studies of demyelination in EAE is the question of the first point of attack of the active agents on the neuro-epithelium. Dr. Appel's studies of affected fragments by means of fluorescence-antibody techniques may serve as an approach to this question (1).

Cultures of rat or mouse cerebellum are exposed for a period of time to the rabbit EAE serum, or to control sera, observed and selected at a chosen moment of their reaction, washed, sometimes fixed, and then overlaid with fluorescein labelled duck anti-rabbit-globulin or anti-rabbit-albumin globulin. The preparations are then viewed in a microscope illuminated by ultra-violet light.

In cultures selected shortly after their exposure to EAE sera, *i.e.*, before demyelination is too advanced, the anti-globulin preparations attach to the neuroglial cell membranes and the myelin sheaths, as demonstrated by the location of fluorescence. If the demyelination is allowed to proceed, the globulins are no longer situated exclusively on the cell membranes, but are found diffusely present within the glial cytoplasm.

If anti-rabbit-albumin globulin is applied after exposure to EAE sera, a different pattern appears—an intracytoplasmic punctate collection of the foreign protein. The same picture emerges from tissues exposed to normal rabbit sera whether one overlays with anti-albumin or anti-globulin duck globulin. This type of reaction has been previously demonstrated by Dr. Igor Klatzo (5) and is thought to represent the incorporation of protein into neuroglia and microglia by pinocytosis.

Finally, a demyelinated culture washed free of EAE serum and returned to normal *in vitro* conditions for a number of days, may reveal a very light trace of rabbit globulin still outlining the neuroglial cell membranes.

From these studies, therefore, we think it possible that the first point of attack of the encephalotoxic factors in EAE sera may be the neuroglial cell membrane and the myelin sheath which, from electron microscopic examinations, has been demonstrated to be composed of modified glial cell membrane.

REFERENCES

1. Appel, S. H., Bornstein, M. B., Seegal, B. C., and Murray, M. R. The Application of Tissue Culture to the Study of Experimental "Allergic" Encephalomyelitis. Immunologic Mechanisms. *IV Internat. Congress of Neuropathology*. Vol. III (In press.).

2. Bornstein, M. B., and Appel, S. H. The Application of Tissue Culture to the Study of Experimental "Allergic" Encephalomyelitis. I. Patterns of Demyelination. *J. Neuropath. and Exper. Neurol., 20:* 141 (1961).

3. Bornstein, M. B., Appel, S. H., and Murray, M. R. The Application of Tissue Culture to the Study of Experimental "Allergic" Encephalomyelitis. Demyelination and Remyelination. *Proc. IV Internat. Congress of Neuropathology*. Vol. III (In press.).

4. Bornstein, M. B., and Murray, M. R. Serial Observations on Patterns of Growth, Myelin Formation, Maintenance and Degeneration in Cultures of Newborn Rat and Kitten Cerebellum. *J. Biophys. and Biochem. Cytol., 4:* 499 (1958).

5. Klatzo, I., and Miquel, J. Observations on Pinocytosis in Nervous Tissue. *J. Neuropath. and Exper. Neurol., 19:* 475 (1960).

6. Luse, S. A. Formation of Myelin in the Central Nervous System of Mice and Rats as Studied with the Electron Microscope. *J. Biophys. and Biochem. Cytol., 2:* 777 (1956).

7. Ross, L., Bornstein, M., and Lehrer, G. Electron Microscopic Observations of Myelin Sheath Formation in Tissue Cultures of Rat Cerebellum. *Anat Rec., 135-6:* 268 (1960). *J. Biophys. and Biochem. Cytol.* (In press.)

Ionic Transport across Neural and Non-Neural Membranes

Harry Grundfest

The Ionic Theory

The ionic, or membrane theory of bioelectricity originated with Bernstein's attempt in 1902 (cf. 7) to account for the negativity inside muscle and nerve cells relative to their outside. This explanation of the *resting potential* was based on the then recently developed theory of semi-permeable membranes and is no longer acceptable in the totality. However, Bernstein also contributed a suggestion which has been amply verified during the past quarter-century, that living membranes could change their permeability characteristics when excited by a stimulus. Thus, he was able to regard the electrogenic responses of all excitable cells, nerves and muscles, sensory and electric organs and glands as changes of the membrane potential from its resting state. As we shall see, these changes can be *depolarizing* or *hyperpolarizing* (repolarizing) in sign, but the former, particularly those which result in an all-or-none action potential or spike, are the more prominent and have been the most studied.

The ionic theory has been very much amplified and improved during the past decade. Largely through the work of Hodgkin and his colleagues (cf. 35), it now provides a remarkably coherent theory which accounts quantitatively for the spike in squid giant axons and to some degree also in several types of nerve and muscle cells. Other theories have also been proposed (cf. 43, 47, 51, 53), and the occurrence of several types of

Supported in part by grants from the Muscular Dystrophy Associations of America, Inc., National Institute of Neurological Diseases and Blindness (Grant B-389 C5, and Grant B-3270), National Science Foundation (G-5665) and United Cerebral Palsy Research and Educational Foundation.

71

"anomalous" responses has prompted a questioning (41, 49) of the validity of the ionic theory. However, the latter theory, too, can account for the anomalous phenomena (28). Furthermore, it also copes, as other theories do not attempt to, with numerous varieties of bioelectric activities which have been disclosed by the recent discovery that there exist two classes of electrogenic membrane, each with several types and sub-types (cf. 21, 26, 28, 29; cf. also Fig. 10).

Ionic inequalities. The ionic theory is based on the fact that most and perhaps all cells have very unequal distribution of ions between the interior of the cell and its external milieu. As a general rule, the interior is some 10 to 100 times richer in K^+ and about 10 times poorer in Na^+. These inequalities probably arise from the action of metabolically driven "ion pumps" which extrude Na^+ and take in K^+. The pumps probably reside in the cell membrane, but the nature of the pumping mechanisms is not yet known (cf. 57). It is obvious, however, that in order to transport the ions against their existing high concentration gradients, the cell must expend considerable energy.

The resting potential. As a result of the inequalities in the distribution of ions and of the presence within the cell of a large quantity of non-diffusible anions, the cell membrane is electrically polarized, inside-negative. In some cells, the magnitude of the resting potential is given by a simple relation between internal and external K^+ (K^+_i and K^+_o as they are written in the formula, respectively):

$$(1) \qquad E_M = 58\,mV \quad \cdot \quad \log \frac{K^+_i}{K^+_o}$$

This relation can be expected to hold only if the permeability of the membrane to other ions is negligible, and if transient effects due to redistribution of ions are thereby excluded. In most cells, however, these factors cannot be neglected. The resting potential may then be expressed by an approximation equation (cf. 18, 38):

$$(2) \qquad E_M = 58\,mV \quad \cdot \quad \log \frac{P_k\,K^+_i + P_{na}\,Na^+_i + P_{cl}\,Cl^-_o}{P_k\,K^+_o + P_{na}\,Na^+_o + P_{cl}\,Cl^-_i}$$

Passive and active electrical phenomena. Thus, two kinds of electrical manifestations might be elicited by changes of the resting potential of the cell. One, a passive diffusional phenomenon would result from a change in the internal or external concentrations of one or several ion species. A similar change also occurs in non-living electrochemical systems, and should therefore be manifested by various types of cells (cf. 15, 47). The initial properties of the membrane remain unchanged during the changes in the ionic distribution and electrical conditions. A second type of electrical manifestation would result from a change in the permeability coefficients P_k, P_{na}, P_{cl} (Equation 2). These phenomena are active processes since they are evoked as a response of the membrane to various stimuli which cause the membrane to change its permeability for one or several ion species. The changes may result from increase or decrease of the permeability coefficients, although electrical changes that result from an increase are far more prominent. They occur in the classical excitable tissues, neurons, muscle fibers, electroplaques, secretory and receptor cells.

The nature of the transducer actions (20) which cause the changes in permeability of the cell membrane is also as yet unknown. However, recent data have shown (21, 26) that two classes of transducer actions exist. One class is initiated by electrical stimuli, and is that found in spike-generating conductile membrane. The other class occurs in receptor or transmissional membranes, which do not react to electrical stimuli, but respond to one or several types of specific stimuli: the nerve impulse, chemical agents, mechanical, photic or thermal energy. The two classes of electrogenic membrane may be further subdivided, and their electrogenic manifestations may be ascribed to participation of different ionic processes. As already noted, the range of phenomena that can be accounted for by the ionic theory is far broader than is the compass of other presently available explanations.

Ionic Determinants of the Resting Potential

According to the ionic theory the metabolically generated unequal distributions of ions constitute the potential energy for the reactive electrogenic processes of excitable cells. When the membrane changes its permeability for one or several ions in response to a stimulus, the ions in question tend to redistribute themselves as dictated by the concentration gradients. The membrane potential changes correspondingly with the influx and/or efflux of the ionic charges. Thus, the resting potential may be regarded as the electrical substrate of other bioelectric manifestations.

Homologous cells in closely related forms may differ markedly with respect to their passive diffusional properties (Fig. 1). Lobster muscle fibers change their resting potential in conformity with Equation 1, the slope of the relation representing a decrease of 58 mV for a 10-fold increase of external K^+. Under the same experimental conditions, however, crayfish muscle fibers show a very different and complex relation between E_M and K^+_o. The E_M-log K^+_o relation of crayfish muscle fibers becomes linear (Fig. 2) with the theoretically predicted slope of 58 mV/decade

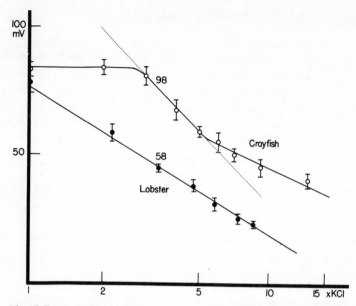

Fig. 1. The different relations between membrane potential, E_M (*ordinate*) and external concentration of K^+ (*abscissa*, expressed on a logarithmic scale as the increase in KCl relative to the initial concentration) for lobster and crayfish muscle fibers. The experimental conditions were identical, but the initial concentrations of K^+_o were those of their normal Ringer's solutions: 15.1 meq/l for lobster and 5.3 meq/l for crayfish. (From ref. 17)

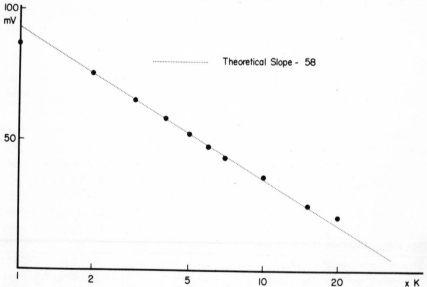

Fig. 2. The E_M-log K^+_o relation of crayfish muscle fibers when the product $(K^+_o)(Cl^-_o)=$ constant. As K^+_o was increased Cl^-_o was diminished by substitution of Na-propionate for NaCl. Otherwise the experimental conditions were the same as those for Fig. 1. (From ref. 17)

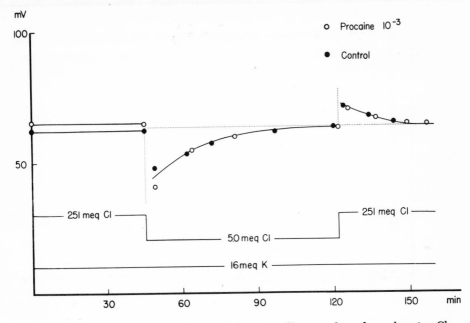

Fig. 3.   Transient effects on E_M of crayfish muscle fibers resulting from changing Cl^-_o.
The depolarization caused by the decrease of Cl^-_o indicates an efflux of Cl^-.
The return to the initial resting potential represents an equilibration of the internal
ionic milieu with K^+_i diminishing as Cl^-_i decreased. The hyperpolarization which was
then produced on returning the preparation to the initial, high Cl^-_o solution represents
the influx of Cl^- and an accompanying influx of K^+. Under the experimental conditions
described by the two lower lines of the figure, procaine did not affect the Cl^- transient
curve, although (cf. Fig. 14) it modifies the response to electrical stimulation markedly.
(From ref. 17)

change in K^+_o when the ionic product (K^+_o) (Cl^-_o) is maintained constant,
by substituting a non-diffusible anion for Cl^-_o in appropriate concentrations.
This effect indicates that in crayfish muscle fibers, as in frog skeletal muscle
(9, 36) the permeability of Cl^- cannot be neglected. This is further shown
by a predictable transient change in resting potential when the external Cl^-
is changed in either direction (Fig. 3). The Cl^--permeability of the membrane can be increased (Fig. 4) by γ-aminobutyric acid (GABA), and
decreased (Fig. 5) by picrotoxin. These effects are distinguishable from
the synaptic actions of the two drugs (32) and are to be ascribed to
actions on the non-synaptic membrane. Thus, similarities in effects of the
drugs on both synaptic and non-synaptic membrane indicate that the membrane structures which permit passage of Cl^- probably have a similar chemical composition in both classes of membrane in some respects, but differ
in others.

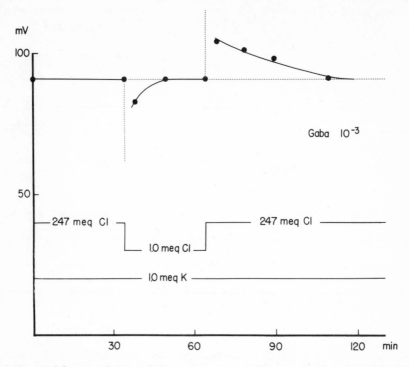

Gaba 10^{-3}

247 meq Cl

1.0 meq Cl

247 meq Cl

1.0 meq Cl

1.0 meq K

FIG. 4.   Modification of Cl^{-}-transient response of crayfish muscle fibers by GABA. The duration of the depolarizing transient change was much briefer than that seen in Fig. 3. This indicates that Cl^{-}-efflux is much more rapid in the presence of GABA. The slow subsidence of the hyperpolarizing transient is an effect independent of the action of GABA, and is due to the low outward (rectifying) conductance of K^{+} when K$^{+}_{o}$ is low. K$^{+}_{o}$ was 1.0 meq/l in this experiment, as indicated on the lowest line of the graph. (From ref. 17)

FIG. 5.   Modification of the Cl^{-}-transient response of crayfish muscle fibers by picrotoxin. The diminution and prolongation of the changes in E_{M} indicate that the drug markedly diminished Cl^{-}-permeability. (From ref. 17)

FIG. 6.   Changes which indicate pharmacological K-inactivation. *Graph*: A lobster muscle fiber became less sensitive to changes in K$^{+}_{o}$, the slope changing from 52 mV to 35 mV/decade change in K$^{+}_{o}$ on treatment with TEA. *Records*: A toad axon which had been depolarized by 35 meq K$^{+}_{o}$ was repolarized when the solution also contained 20 meq TEA. (From ref. 28, after refs. 55 and 50 respectively)

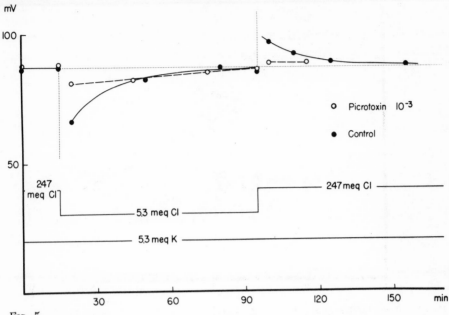

FIG. 5.

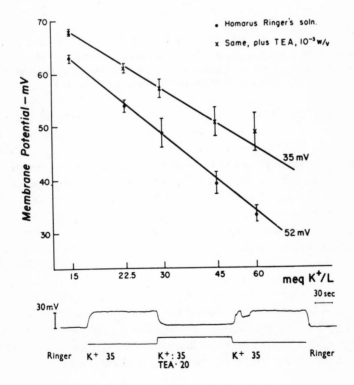

FIG. 6.

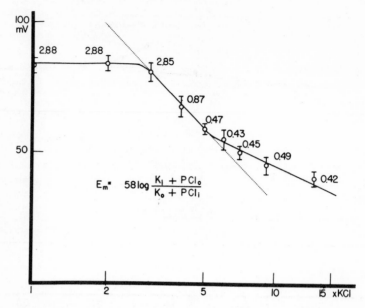

F$_{IG}$. 7.   Reproduction of the E_M-log K^+_o curve of crayfish muscle fibers by assuming
a change in the relative permeability coefficient $P = \dfrac{P_{cl}}{P_k}$ of the equation shown in the
inset. The points are experimental values (Fig. 1), the bars indicating 95% confidence limits.
The continuous line was calculated assuming values of P shown on the graph. At a
4-fold increase of K^+_o P changed about 3-fold and thereafter was constant and 6 to
7-fold smaller than the initial value. (From ref. 17)

The pharmacological modification of Cl$^-$-permeability is independent
of the permeability to K$^+$. The latter can also be modified pharmacologically
independently of Cl$^-$-permeability (Fig. 6). Thus, the passive diffusional
channels for K$^+$ and Cl$^-$ appear to be distinct. These data suggest therefore:
(a) that the membrane has a number of channels of appropriate size to
pass ions of the dimensions of K$^+$ and Cl$^-$, and (b) that some of these
channels furthermore probably have a net negative charge and are selective for K$^+$ while others, with net positive charge, serve as channels for Cl$^-$.
The different pharmacological properties of the two kinds of channels presumably relate to the type of chemical structures which result in the
negative and positive charges.

The complex form of the E_M–log K^+_o curve of crayfish muscle fibers
(Fig. 1) can be readily reproduced from a simple modification of Equation 2 (Fig. 7). This calculation assumes that P_{cl} initially is about 3 times
as large as P_k, but that P_k becomes more than twice as large as P_{cl} at higher
concentrations of K^+_o. The total shift of P_k is about 7-fold.

Ionic Processes of the Active Membrane

Varieties of change in membrane permeability. The data embodied in Figure 7 indicate that in the presence of high K^+_o (or of some threshold depolarization), P_k of crayfish muscle fibers increased about 7-fold. Thus the complex relation between resting potential and K^+_o of Figures 1 and 7 is already a manifestation of a reactive change in membrane permeability. The most general description of these changes is given by the changed impedance of the cell membrane as a result of the transducer actions. Electrogenic phenomena are most prominent when there is a large increase in permeability (12, 37). However, considerable increase in conductance may occur (Fig. 8) indicating increased permeability to some ions, without marked electrogenic manifestations. Yet, these same conductance changes can also result in considerable electrogenesis under appropriate electrochemical conditions (cf. Fig. 12).

Varieties of changes in membrane resistance. The impedance changes may be summarized in two sets of relations between applied current and membrane voltage (Fig. 9). The I-E relation is linear for electrically inexcitable electrogenic membranes. Thus, the membranes behave as passive

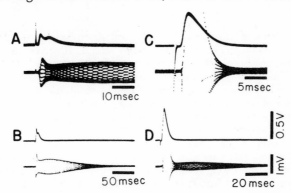

Fig. 8. Conductance changes during electrogenic activity. *Raia* electric organ. (A, B) *R. erinacea;* two speeds of registration. (C, D) *R. eglantaria. Upper trace in each set* is the potential recorded across the organ on stimulating its nerve supply. This depolarizing response which is electrically inexcitable was considerably larger in *R. eglantaria. The lower trace in each set* shows the imbalance in an a.c. bridge (of which the organ formed one arm) when the response occurred. The depolarizing electrogenesis in both organs was associated with an imbalance due to increased conductance. A subsequent phase of increased conductance was relatively much larger in *R. erinacea* than in *R. eglantaria.* This change is due to increased Cl-conductance produced in an electrically excitable component of the cell membrane. Although the conductance change was large, it caused relatively little change in membrane potential. However, as shown in Fig. 12, under different electrochemical conditions it could produce a marked depolarization. (Modified from ref. 4)

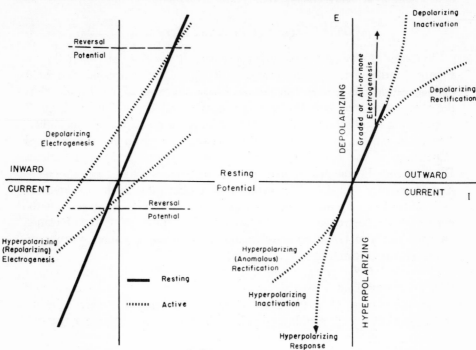

FIG. 9. I-E relations of electrogenic membranes. *Electrically inexcitable membranes* behave as ohmic resistances, E changing linearly with I. However, the slope changes during activation of the membrane by an appropriate stimulus. The broken lines represent active membrane of excitatory (depolarizing) and inhibitory (repolarizing or hyperpolarizing) synapses. A characteristic feature of electrically inexcitable electrogenesis is its reversal when E exceeds the reversal potential specified by the intersection of the resistance lines for active and passive membrane. *Electrically excitable membranes* may exhibit one or several varieties of conductance change. Most, but not all, develop graded or all-or-none depolarizing responses which are accompanied by increased membrane conductance and thus represent a negative resistance characteristic. Increased conductance due to depolarizing rectification is shown in Fig. 8, and that due to hyperpolarizing (anomalous) rectification is shown in Figs. 14, 21 and 22. Decreased conductance by depolarizing inactivation is shown in Figs. 18 and 19, and that by hyperpolarizing inactivation with production of hyperpolarizing responses is seen in Figs. 20 to 22. Pharmacological inactivation (not shown in the diagram) is illustrated in Figs. 5, 6, 13-15 and 21.

resistive components with a constant resistance for electrical currents of different magnitudes. The resistance decreases during excitation of these membranes by specific stimuli, and that decrease results in depolarizing or repolarizing (hyperpolarizing) electrically inexcitable electrogenesis (21, 26, 28). Pharmacological agents (synapse inactivator drugs) diminish or eliminate the reactivity of electrically inexcitable membranes (22, 24, 26, 29).

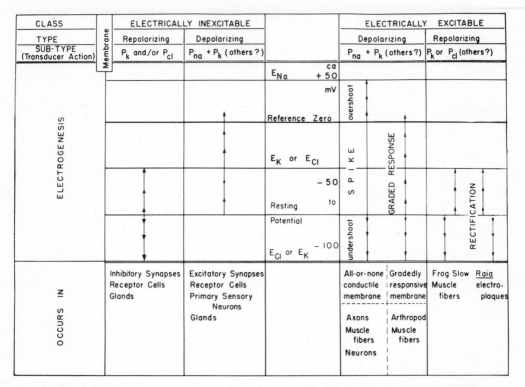

FIG. 10. The probable ionic components of different electrogenic activities. The resting potential is represented as lying between E_K and E_{Cl}, the electrode potentials for
K+ and Cl- respectively. E_{Na}, the electrode potential for Na+ is indicated as about 50 mV
positive to the reference zero. The two classes of differently excitable membranes are
each subdivided into electrogenic types and into sub-types characterized by the nature
of their transducer actions which lead to increased permeability (P_k, P_{cl}, P_{na}) for
different ion species. The types of cells or cell components in which the different activities occur are also shown. The membranes could be further subdivided by various
pharmacological reactions, as described in the text.

The current-voltage relations of electrically excitable membrane are
much more complex, reflecting the reactivity of the membrane to changes
of the potential across it. Besides the large conductance increase which
takes place during depolarizing electrogenesis, depolarizing and hyperpolarizing currents may initiate changes to decrease the resistance (rectification and anomalous rectification, respectively) or to increase it (depolarizing and hyperpolarizing inactivation), but with little or no change
in membrane potential. Some of these effects play important roles in various
"anomalous" bioelectric phenomena (28).

Ionic phenomena associated with increased membrane conductance.
Transducer actions of electrogenic membranes which cause increase of the

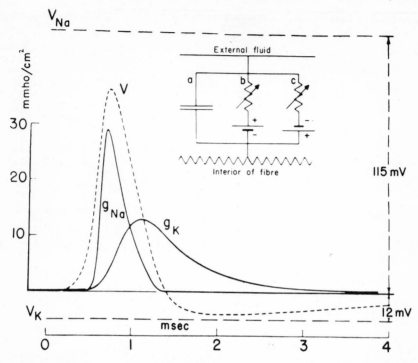

F<small>IG</small>. 11. Analysis of the spike of the squid giant axon (V, broken line) in terms of the Hodgkin-Huxley theory. The inset diagram shows the equivalent circuit. A depolarizing stimulus initiates Na-activation, which increases conductance for that ion (g_{Na}), also shown in branch c of the inset. The sodium battery (V_{Na}) is inside positive. A process of Na-inactivation is assumed to diminish g_{Na} rapidly from its maximum value. A slower rise in g_K, caused by K-activation, outlasts g_{Na} and after the repolarization of the axon is responsible for a temporary hyperpolarization nearly to the full value of the potassium battery (V_K). When the net change in charge on the membrane capacity is inside positive due to greater influx of Na+ than efflux of K+ the membrane potential is depolarizing. (Redrawn from ref. 13)

permeability of the membrane for specific ions can cause various types of electrogenic manifestations (Fig. 10). A symmetrical pattern of changes exists in the electrically excitable and electrically inexcitable membranes. An increase in P_{na} which results in a shift of the potential from its inside negative level toward a decreased internal negativity is characteristic of the depolarizing types of electrogenic membranes of both classes. However, the responses may differ markedly. The electrogenesis in the electrically excitable membrane has a regenerative character (37). The initial influx of Na+ which results from the excitatory depolarization of the membrane adds further depolarization which excites further Na^+ influx, etc. The result may be all-or-none, resulting in a spike (Fig. 11) which represents a reversal of the membrane polarization. The amount of reversal approaches a peak value given by:

$$(3) \qquad E_{Na} = 58 \text{ mV} \cdot \log \frac{Na^+_i}{Na^+_o}$$

This peak is diminished and the spike is terminated by a delayed process of K^+-efflux (K-activation) and a subsidiary process of Na-inactivation (37). Another type of depolarizing electrically excitable electrogenesis which results in graded responses will be described later. The depolarizing electrogenesis of electrically inexcitable membrane (Fig. 8) lacks the regenerative feature of electrically excitable activity and is also a graded response whose amplitude depends upon the amount of excitant agent. Similar depolarizing graded responses are developed in sensory and receptive electrogenesis (25, 27).

Both classes of membranes also occur in varieties which lack the component of Na-conductance (Fig. 10) and involve only K^+ and/or Cl^-. The electrogenesis resulting from the change in P_k or P_{cl} is small and may be insignificant, depending upon the relation of the resting potential to the potentials given by Equation 1 for K^+ and Cl^- respectively. If both P_k and P_{cl} change, the resulting change in potential would be given by Equation 2. Among the electrically inexcitable membranes the inhibitory p.s.p.'s of heart are probably due to changes in P_k (39), those of crustacean neuromuscular i.p.s.p.'s to change in P_{cl} (8, 32), and the p.s.p.'s of crayfish stretch receptors to increases in both P_k and P_{cl} (14, 33).

Two varieties of electrically excitable membranes of the same type are known at present. The electrically excitable rectification of frog slow muscle fibers (10, 42) is due to increased conductance for K^+ (3), while that of *Raia* electroplaques (4, 5, 11, 30) is probably due to increased conductance only for Cl^- (28). This case also provides a very instructive support for the ionic theory. Under the normal conditions of high external Cl^- the rectifying conductance increase is accompanied by little or no electrogenic manifestation (Fig. 8) since influx of Cl^- can change the potential very little (Fig. 10). However, when *Raia* electroplaques are bathed in Cl^--free medium, a depolarizing electrical stimulus must cause efflux of Cl^- and the resulting depolarization can then be regenerative as it is during the influx of Na^+ in spike activity. This response of the *Raia* electroplaques (Fig. 12) results in a "spike" of some 40 mV depolarization lasting for a considerable time, until the conductance increase is terminated by a process of depolarizing Cl-inactivation.

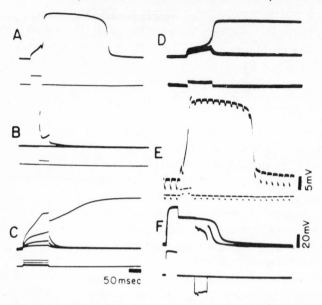

FIG. 12.   Depolarizing electrically excitable electrogenesis manifested by electroplaques of *Raia erinacea* when Cl^-_o is removed. The normal response of the electroplaques to a brief depolarizing pulse (B) is a brief large depolarization and a smaller later depolarization when the rectifying conductance increase becomes maximal. When the current is terminated there may be a subsequent depolarization, but only of a few mV. In the absence of Cl^-_o the response becomes a prolonged "spike" which long outlasts the stimulus (A). The "spike" has a threshold (C) and is all-or-none (D). It is associated with increased conductance (E) and is abolished by hyperpolarizing currents (F). Its maximal amplitude is about 40 mV depolarization and it may last for more than 0.5 sec. The "spike" is due to regenerative depolarization initiated and maintained by efflux of Cl^-. (From ref. 11, and unpublished data)

Structural implications of the occurrence of different ion-valving components. The possibility for occurrence of membranes in which the permeability may change only for one of the ion species, or for several, indicates that ion channels made available by the transducer actions are specific. Thus permeability increase for Na^+ might be made possible by opening of negatively charged channels of a different size from those for K^+, while, as already noted, the occurrence of active channels only for K^+ or for Cl^- indicate that the channels may be exclusively or predominantly either negatively or positively charged. Furthermore, the presence of the same types and sub-types of ionic phenomena in the two classes of differently excitable membranes indicates another order of molecular differences which determine whether the changes from "closed" (inactive) to "open" (active) channels are produced by electrical (electrostatic) or by other types of distortion (*e.g.,* by chemical forces in synaptic membranes; me-

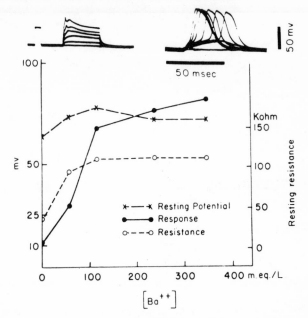

Fɪɢ. 13. Effects of Ba++ on electrophysiological properties of lobster muscle fibers. *Inset records*:

(*Left*) Before applying Ba++. Sequence of superimposed records of membrane potential in one fiber on applying progressively increasing current pulses of 60 msec. duration through an intracellular microelectrode. Calibrating pulse at beginning of traces is 50 mV and 10 msec. A threshold response is seen in the third trace from the top, and a maximal response is shown in the highest trace. Note the decreasing latency as well as the increased amplitude of the response. The latter shows an undershoot indicative of delayed rectification. The rectification is also indicated by the fall of the membrane depolarization from its initial peak.

(*Right*) After applying 115 meq. Ba++/liter to another muscle fiber. The superimposed traces show the effects of increasing strengths of intracellularly applied 30 msec. depolarizing pulses. The weakest stimulus failed to evoke a spike. The response evoked by the next stronger pulse occurred immediately after the end of the stimulus. The increasingly stronger stimuli evoked responses with briefer latencies, but of the same amplitude and form.

(*Below*) The effect of increasing concentrations of Ba++ on the resting potential, resting effective resistance, and maximum response amplitude. Effective resistance scale on the right ordinate. The potential scale on the left applies to response amplitude as well as resting potentials. In this preparation the all-or-none response did not develop an overshoot until 30% of the Na+ had been replaced with Ba++. (From ref. 55)

chanical in Pacinian corpuscles, stretch receptors or other mechanoceptive membranes).

Differences between passive and activated channels. Growing comparative pharmacological data on a variety of cells disclose further distinctions in the properties of the channels for various ions. Thus, tetra-

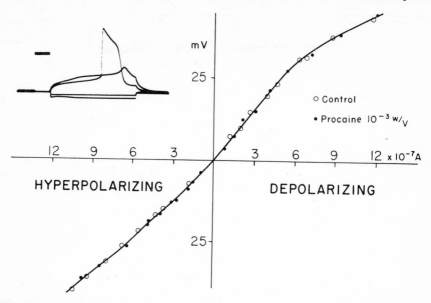

Fɪɢ. 14. Conversion of graded to all-or-none responsiveness without alteration of membrane resistance or resting potential. Crayfish muscle fiber. *Inset:* Superimposed records of intracellularly applied depolarizing currents (two traces; downward deflection) and of the resulting responses (traces with upward deflection). Before applying procaine, the larger current evoked a small late potential which was the maximal graded response of the fiber. After applying procaine, the weak stimulus evoked a spike, which had a characteristic long time course and a plateau. Calibration 50 mV and 100msec. The graph shows that the complex I-E relation of the same muscle fiber was not affected by procaine. (From ref. 17)

ethyl ammonium (TEA) and alkali-earth ions increase the resting membrane resistance of arthropod muscle fibers (55, 56) while at the same time altering the normally graded responses to all-or-none spikes (Fig. 13), and modifying their sensitivity to K^+ (Fig. 6). Similar effects are produced by TEA on toad (50; cf. Fig. 6) and frog (44) nodes. TEA, however, does not change the resting resistance of squid axons (52) or *Onchidium* neurons (34), although it modifies profoundly their electrogenic responses (cf. Fig. 15). A further example of the differentiation between resting and activated channels is given by the effects of procaine on arthropod muscle fibers (Fig. 14). The response to an electrical stimulus is changed from the normal small graded potential to an all-or-none spike. However, the current-voltage relation, which shows the various complexities described in Figure 9, is not affected by procaine.

    Conductance changes evoked in electrically excitable membrane. The active processes associated with spike electrogenesis have been characterized by Hodgkin and Huxley (37) chiefly with the aid of voltage clamp experi-

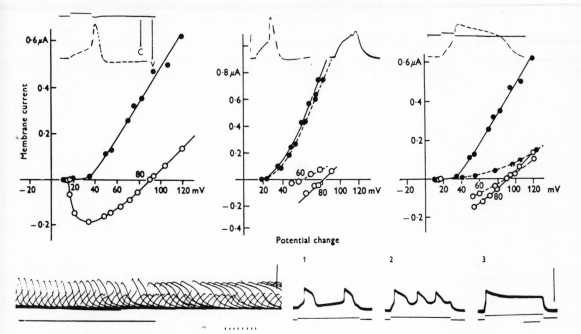

FIG. 15. Differential elimination of Na-activation and K-activation in *Onchidium* neurons. Voltage clamp experiments show the initial inward current (circles) and late outward current (dots) as functions of the membrane potential. Solid lines connect control data; broken lines, after treatment with drugs. Insets show the responses to brief stimuli.

Left: Control series, blanking of potential trace at 5 msec. intervals; calibration 100 mV and 5x10⁻⁷ A.

Center: Neuron in a preparation treated with 2% urethane. Note that the inward (Na⁺) current was markedly diminished, while the outward (K⁺) current was unaffected. The spike of the cell was changed to a small graded potential. Blanking intervals, 2 msec.

Right: From an experiment in which the preparation had been exposed to tetraethylammonium ions (TEA). The K⁺-current was diminished much more than was the Na⁺-current, and the response of the cell became prolonged. Blanking signals at 5 msec. intervals.

Below, left: Development of the prolonged response on applying TEA during a mixing interval indicated by bar line, lower left. Multiple sweeps at 1 per sec., each registering a response evoked by a direct stimulus. Calibration for each sweep 100 mV and 5 msec. intervals.

Below, right: Sample records of responses to prolonged applied currents. Calibrations 100 mV and 100 msec. Lower traces show the stimulating currents. (From ref. 28 after ref. 34)

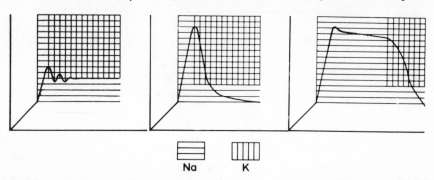

Na   K

Fɪɢ. 16. Principle of conversion of graded responses of arthropod muscle fibers to spikes and to prolonged responses. Inward flux of Na⁺ due to Na-activation is opposed by an early onset of K-conductance and the repolarizing action of K⁺-efflux. Delay of K⁺-efflux permits charging the membrane capacity (cf. Fig. 11) to values closer to the sodium potential.

ments. Similar data on *Onchidium* neurons (Fig. 15) show that the initial component of inward (Na⁺) current can be markedly diminished without seriously affecting a later component of outward (K⁺) current. The resulting change in electrogenesis is from an all-or-none spike to a graded response. TEA, however, diminished most markedly the K⁺-current component and the resulting change in electrogenesis was prolongation of the spike. These effects had been predicted earlier on theoretical grounds (21, 35, 48).

More or less independent modifications of Na- and K-conductance components by various pharmacological agents also lead to conversion of graded responses to all-or-none activity (Figs. 13, 14, and 16), and to prolonged spikes. The occurrence of normally gradedly responsive electrically excitable electrogenesis in many arthropod muscles (2, 32, 55, 56) and its ready conversion to all-or-none responses indicate different quantitative relations between conductance changes for the depolarizing (Na⁺) and repolarizing (K⁺ and/or Cl⁻) electrogenesis. Differences in the dynamic properties of the different conductance components are also indicated by the occurrence of two and sometimes of three varieties of spikes in the same cell. Thus, the electroplaques of *Malapterurus* (40), *Mormyrus rume* (5) and some Gymnotidae (4, 6) develop different spikes in different parts of the cell surface (Fig. 17).

A further difference may be distinguished by the different reactions of squid axons and *Onchidium* neurons to TEA. This agent prolongs the spikes of both cells, but it acts on *Onchidium* neurons when applied externally (34), while it must be injected into squid axons (52). Thus, the membranes of the two neurons appear to have different properties on the inside and outside (19). A related distinction is that indicated by the

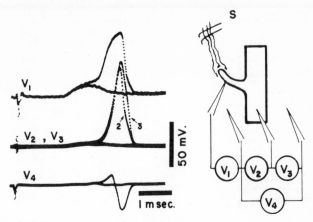

FIG. 17. Different action potentials in different parts of a single electroplaque of the Gymnotid, *Steatogenys*. The electroplaques of this knifefish are innervated at the tip of a short stalk which emerges from the caudal surface of the cell (diagram). Four recording microelectrodes (V_1-V_4) were used to obtain the simultaneous records shown on the left. Each line shows two successive traces of responses to stimulations of the nerve which did and did not evoke spikes. When the spikes failed to arise there was only a p.s.p. which was largest in the recording from the stalk (V_1), since the p.s.p. does not propagate actively from its site of origin at the tip of the stalk. When a spike arose in the stalk it propagated into the cell body, exciting first the caudal face of the latter (registered as V_2) and then the rostral (V_3). The two recording traces, V_2 and V_3, were made coincident to show the shorter duration of the spike in the caudal face. Thus, the electroplaque develops 4 different kinds of action potential: a depolarizing p.s.p. and 3 spikes of different durations. V_4 shows the external potential of the electroplaque. The initial positivity which resulted when the spikes were produced also indicates that the spike of the caudal face arose earlier than did that of the rostral face, but lasted a briefer time than did the spikes of the rostral face, which contributed a large head-negative potential. (Unpublished data of Dr. M. V. L. Bennett)

response of squid axons and arthropod muscle fibers to alkali-earth ions. The latter and many other cells develop prolonged spikes when Ba^{++}, Ca^{++} or Sr^{++} are applied externally. Squid axons do not react in this way. They are irreversibly inactivated by injected alkali-earth ions (31). Lobster muscle fibers are probably similarly affected, since on prolonged soaking in media containing the alkali-earth ions they become depolarized and inexcitable (55).

Phenomena associated with decreased conductance. The electrical manifestations of increased Na^+-, K^+-, and Cl^--permeability are antagonistic, in the sense that the first tends to cause depolarization while the others tend to cause repolarization. Thus, as was shown in connection with Figs. 15 and 16, electrical activity can be modified in either direction; toward less depolarization by increasing K^+- or Cl^--permeability, or by decreasing Na^+-permeability; and toward larger, prolonged depolarizations by in-

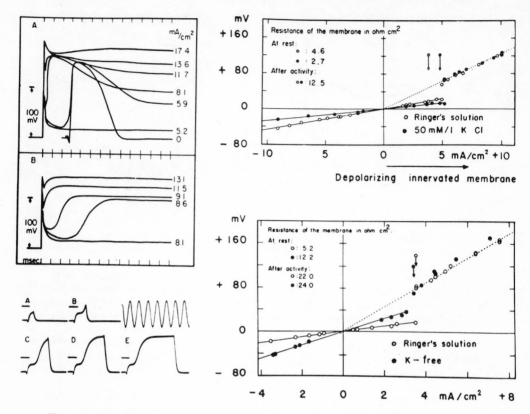

Fɪɢ. 18. Depolarizing K-inactivation in eel electroplaques. *Left:* Potentials across innervated membrane of a single cell recorded during one of the experiments.

(A) A brief pulse (marked O) evoked a spike. The latter was also produced on applying a current of 5.9 mA/cm² to depolarize the innervated membrane. Note, however, that the terminal depolarization was much larger than with a subthreshold stimulus (5.2 mA/cm²). Stronger currents evoked the spike earlier and caused proportionately larger terminal depolarizations. The strongest current (17.4 mA/cm²) caused depolarization which exceeded E_{Na}, the potential showing a temporary reversal.

(B) A similar series of experiments after the preparation had been placed in 50 mM/l K⁺. Spikes were no longer evoked, and the rise in membrane potential, signifying increased membrane resistance, developed slowly. The early large deflections in both sets of records are due to capacitative artifacts.

Below: (A-E) Time course of the delayed rise in potential shown by applying successively longer pulses at constant amplitude.

Right, upper graphs: An experiment like that of (A) and (B) on the left. The arrows indicate the threshold current for the spikes in the control saline solution and for the delayed inactivation process in the high K-solution. *Lower. graphs:* A similar experiment in the standard saline and in a K-free solution. (From ref. 28 after ref. 1)

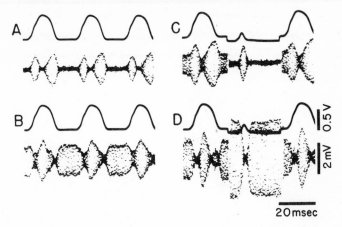

20 msec

FIG. 19. Impedance changes during activity of electric organs of *Sternopygus*, a Gymnotid which emits continuously monophasic, head-positive pulses at frequencies ranging from about 40/sec. to 100/sec., depending on the fish. The upper trace in each set shows the discharges of the fish. The lower traces are of the simultaneously recorded changes in bridge balance when the fish was made one arm of the bridge.

(A) The bridge was initially balanced for zero output during the quiescent period between discharges. It became markedly unbalanced during the rising and falling phases of the discharges in a direction indicating increased conductance.

(B) The bridge was unbalanced so that increased conductance tended to diminish the output. At the peak of each discharge the output was higher than in the period of quiescence, indicating that the resistance of the electroplaques increased during the peak of the discharge.

(C, D) Same as (A) and (B), except that the organ was hyperpolarized briefly to prevent the discharges of the electroplaques. Only p.s.p.'s then appeared and these were associated with an increased conductance, as in Fig. 8. (From ref. 4)

creasing Na^+-permeability relative to that for K^+ or Cl^-. In the conversion of graded to all-or-none responses of arthropod muscles *pharmacological K-inactivation* plays an important role and some agents also block Na-inactivation (55).

Depolarizing K-inactivation. When eel electroplaques are subjected to depolarizing currents the membrane resistance increases even during the falling phase of the spike (Fig. 18), whereas in squid giant axons the resistance is low at this point (Fig. 11). The resistance rise occurs independently of the presence or absence of a Na-conductance increase. It has a delayed time course, but at its maximum the resistance is independent of the initial membrane resistance, which could be that of the resting cell, or the lower value of a cell in high K^+_o, or the higher resistance of a cell in zero K^+_o. The total increase in resistance is some 6-fold and a change of this magnitude is likely only if it involves a decrease in permeability to K^+, or depolarizing K-inactivation (23, 28).

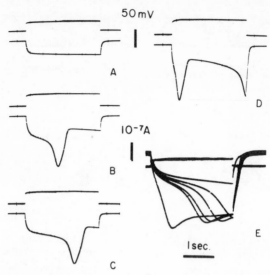

Fɪɢ. 20. Hyperpolarizing responses in lobster muscle fiber. *Upper trace*: Monitor of intracellularly applied hyperpolarizing current. *Lower trace*: Membrane potential.

(A) Current subthreshold for response.

(B, C) Hyperpolarizing responses at threshold show first a slow increase in negativity, then a regenerative rise, and its subsidence to a value less negative than at the start of the hyperpolarizing response.

(D) A stronger current caused earlier onset of the pulse-phase and a second pulse developed before the current was terminated.

(E) Six superimposed records showing variations of responses. (From ref. 46)

Depolarizing K-inactivation may account in part for the plateau of vertebrate cardiac spikes (23, 45) in which the plateau is associated with membrane resistance higher than that of the diastolic level (54). Impedance measurements also demonstrate (Fig. 19) the normal occurrence of an increased membrane resistance during the peak of the spike in electroplaques of some Gymnotidae (4, 6). However, the spikes of the electroplaques are not significantly prolonged by the K-inactivation, as are the cardiac spikes, partly because the time constant of the electroplaque membrane is very small (23). Thus, the depolarization induced by the conductance changes can be dissipated rapidly in the electroplaques even if an active repolarizing process has not intervened. Repolarizing activity may actually be absent in eel electroplaques, but in *Sternopygus* (Fig. 19) there is an increased conductance in the falling phase of the spike. It does not occur when only the p.s.p. is present and therefore is a conductance increase of electrically excitable membrane which has a repolarizing electrogenesis.

Hyperpolarizing K-inactivation. The membrane resistance may also increase when very strong hyperpolarizing currents are applied (46). Then,

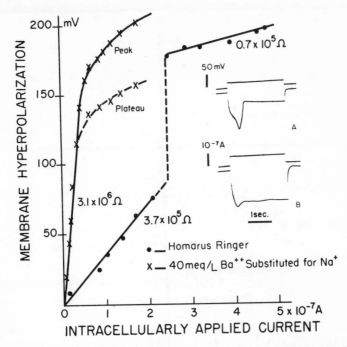

FIG. 21. Abolition of hyperpolarizing responses of lobster muscle fibers by alkali-earth ions. *Inset*: Records of hyperpolarizing response in *Homarus* saline (A) and its absence (B) in a high (4×) Ca++ medium. *Graphs*: Current-voltage curves for another muscle fiber in the normal Ringer's medium (dots) and in a high Ba++ medium (crosses). Development of a hyperpolarizing response in the Ringer's solution is denoted by the sudden rise of the peak membrane hyperpolarization when the applied current exceeded about 2.5x10⁻⁷ A. Note that higher currents caused relatively little further change in the peak potential, indicating a low dynamic resistance. On applying Ba++ the effective resistance increased nearly 9-fold, and a hyperpolarizing response did not develop. Higher currents produced lower additional hyperpolarizations both in the early peak and in the plateau, indicating that hyperpolarizing conductance increase was still present. (From ref. 46)

while the applied current remains constant, the membrane potential becomes much more strongly inside-negative. The change may subside spontaneously while the current is still being applied, and the membrane potential then also becomes less negative. One or several spike-like "hyperpolarizing responses" can thus appear during application of a constant current (Fig. 20).

These oscillatory effects are due to a complex of conductance changes, the primary of which is a decreased permeability for K⁺. On this hyperpolarizing K-inactivation may be superimposed increased conductance for Na⁺ and/or Cl⁻ (46). When the membrane resistance is already high (indicating low permeability for K⁺) or is increased by pharmacological

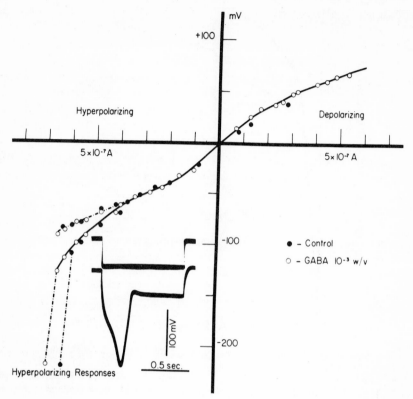

FIG. 22. Hyperpolarizing responses in crayfish muscle fibers. Two preparations which had been soaked overnight in a Cl⁻-free Ringer's solution. Cl^-_i was then practically absent, as well as Cl^-_o, so that addition of GABA to one of the preparations did not change the I-E curve. The latter was similar in the depolarizing quadrant to that shown in Fig. 14. In the hyperpolarizing quadrant the initial portions of the curves were also similar. The potentials would resemble that seen in the inset record B of Fig. 21 for a lobster muscle fiber treated with alkali-earth ions. The solid line in Fig. 22 shows the initial potential and the broken line the later steady value. In the absence of Cl⁻, however, hyperpolarizing responses were obtained (inset record) which are never seen in crayfish muscle fibers in normal Ringer's solution. The upper trace of the inset records show the applied current (0.6 μA). (From ref. 17)

K-inactivation, the hyperpolarizing K-inactivation and the pulse-like hyperpolarizing response are eliminated (Fig. 21), but the secondary, increased conductance remains.

Hyperpolarizing responses are readily manifested in those cells (*e.g.,* lobster muscle fibers, Figs. 20, 21) in which K⁺-permeability is initially high, but they can also be produced in other cells, such as squid, frog or toad axons, by first raising the K⁺-permeability by depolarizing the cells in a medium high in K⁺ (28). In crayfish muscle fibers the hyperpolarizing responses do not normally occur, because the secondary conductance increase (involving Cl^-) is very large and occurs rapidly (16). However, under appropriate experimental conditions crayfish muscle fibers also develop a hyperpolarizing response (Fig. 22).

Effects of independent assortment of different conductance changes. The foregoing examples have shown that electrogenic membranes can undergo both activation and inactivation phenomena for different ion species, and that these various changes can occur independently, in various combinations. When one or another of these effects operates alone, or is predominant, the bioelectric results may be relatively simple. However, when these various ionic changes occur in combinations the effects may be quite startling and can appear to be contrary to the laws of classical electrophysiology. Thus, there are various "anomalous" phenomena (cf. 28, 49) such as "upside-down" spikes or prolonged, or oscillating spikes. Quantitative data for the analysis of most of these phenomena are still inadequate. However, the nature of these manifestations as resulting from relative changes in membrane permeability for different ions can already be discerned (28).

Possible applications in neurology. The gap between our knowledge of fundamental mechanisms of bioelectric activity and of its applications to clinical material is still wide. However, this no longer stems entirely from our ignorance of the basic mechanisms. It seems to me likely that basic data are now available which could be put to use in analyzing several varieties of neuromuscular disorders. The difficulty is no longer one of deficient theoretical concepts, but resides in the paucity of personnel trained to develop the techniques necessary to investigate the clinical material with the methods and concepts that the fundamental research has developed regarding the electrophysiology and pharmacology of electrogenic membranes.

Summary

The ionic theory of bioelectrogenesis is applicable to both classes of electrogenic membrane, those which are electrically excitable and those which are electrically inexcitable. It further characterizes the different types and sub-types of electrogenesis within the two classes. The electrical manifestations of living membranes encompass not only passive, diffusional changes in membrane potential, but also active processes. The living electrogenic membranes may change their permeability characteristics for one or for several ion species, and the change may be toward increased or decreased permeability. These different processes may run concurrently and may be modified independently. The effects of different combinations and permutations of these functionally interacting processes can now be analyzed in considerable detail, and might provide clues to some pathological conditions.

REFERENCES

1. Altamirano, M., and Coates, C. W. Effect of potassium on electroplax of *Electrophorus electricus. J. Cell. and Comp. Physiol., 49:* 69-102 (1957).
2. Belton, P., and Grundfest, H. Comparative effects of drugs on graded responses of insect muscle fibers. *Fed. Proc., 20:* 339 (1961).
3. Belton, P., and Grundfest, H. The ionic mechanism of rectification in frog slow muscle fibers. *Biol. Bull., 121:* 382 (1961).
4. Bennett, M. V. L. Modes of operation of electric organs. *Ann. N. Y. Acad. Sci., 94:* 458-509 (1961).
5. Bennett, M. V. L., and Grundfest, H. Studies on morphology and electrophysiology of electric organs. III. Electrophysiology of electric organs in Mormyrids. In *Bioelectrogenesis* (C. Chagas and A. Paes de Carvalho, Eds.), Elsevier, Amsterdam, 1961.
6. Bennett, M. V. L., and Grundfest, H. Unpublished data.
7. Bernstein, J. *Electrobiologie.* F. Vieweg, Braunschweig, 1912.
8. Boistel, J., and Fatt, P. Membrane permeability change during inhibitory transmitter action in crustacean muscle. *J. Physiol., 144:* 176-191 (1958).
9. Boyle, P. J., and Conway, E. J. Potassium accumulation in muscle and associated changes. *J. Physiol.* (Lond.), *100:* 1-63 (1941).
10. Burke, W., and Ginsborg, B. L. The electrical properties of the slow muscle fibre membrane. *J. Physiol.* (Lond.), *132:* 586-598 (1956).
11. Cohen, B., Bennett, M. V. L., and Grundfest, H. Electrically excitable responses in *Raia erinacea* electroplaques. *Fed. Proc., 20:* 339 (1961).
12. Cole, K. S., and Curtis, H. J. Electric impedance of the squid giant axon during activity. *J. Gen. Physiol., 22:* 649-670 (1939).
13. Eccles, J. C. Neuron physiology. In *Handbook of Physiology, I. Neurophysiology I.* (J. Field, Ed.), American Physiological Society, Washington, D. C., 1959.
14. Edwards, C., and Hagiwara, S. Potassium ions and the inhibitory process in the crayfish stretch receptor. *J. Gen. Physiol., 43:* 315-321 (1959).
15. Giebisch, G. Measurements of electrical potential differences on single nephrons of the perfused *Necturus* kidney. *J. Gen. Physiol., 44:* 659-678 (1961).
16. Girardier, L., Reuben, J. P., and Grundfest, H. Components of the resting potential in crayfish and lobster muscle fibers. *Biol. Bull., 121:* 366 (1961).

17. Girardier, L., Reuben, J. P., and Grundfest, H. Unpublished data.
18. Goldman, D. E. Potential, impedance, and rectification in membranes. *J. Gen. Physiol.*, *27:* 37-60 (1943).
19. Grundfest, H. The nature of the electrochemical potentials of bioelectric tissues. In, *Electrochemistry in Biology and Medicine* (T. Shedlovsky, Ed.), John Wiley, New York, 1955.
20. Grundfest, H. Excitation triggers in post-junctional cells. In, *Physiological Triggers* (T. H. Bullock, Ed.), American Physiological Society, Washington, D. C., 1957.
21. Grundfest, H. Electrical inexcitability of synapses and some of its consequences in the central nervous system. *Physiol. Revs.*, *37:* 337-361 (1957).
22. Grundfest, H. General problems of drug action on bioelectric phenomena. *Ann. N. Y. Acad. Sci.*, *66:* 537-591 (1957).
23. Grundfest, H. The mechanisms of discharge of the electric organs in relation to general and comparative electrophysiology. *Prog. Biophys.*, *7:* 1-85 (1957).
24. Grundfest, H. An electrophysiological basis for neuropharmacology. *Fed. Proc.*, *17:* 1006-1018 (1958).
25. Grundfest, H. Evolution of conduction in the nervous system. In, *Evolution of Nervous Control* (A. D. Bass, Ed.), American Association for the Advancement of Science, Washington, D. C., 1959.
26. Grundfest, H. Synaptic and ephaptic transmission. In, *Handbook of Physiology, Section 1, Neurophysiology I* (J. Field, Ed.), American Physiological Society, Washington, D. C., 1959.
27. Grundfest, H. Excitation by hyperpolarizing potentials. A general theory of receptor activities. In, *Nervous Inhibition* (E. Florey, Ed.), Pergamon Press, London, 1961.
28. Grundfest, H. Ionic mechanisms in electrogenesis. *Ann. N. Y. Acad. Sci.*, *94:* 405-457 (1961).
29. Grundfest, H. General physiology and pharmacology of junctional transmission. In, *Biophysics of Physiological and Pharmacological Actions* (A. M. Shanes, Ed.), American Association for the Advancement of Science, Washington, D. C., 1961.
30. Grundfest, H., and Bennett, M. V. L. Studies on morphology and electrophysiology of electric organs. I. Electrophysiology of marine electric fishes. In, *Bioelectrogenesis* (C. Chagas and A. Paes de Carvalho, Eds.), Elsevier, Amsterdam, 1961.
31. Grundfest, H., Kao, C. Y., and Altamirano, M. Bioelectric effects of ions microinjected into the giant axon of *Loligo. J. Gen. Physiol.*, *38:* 245-282 (1954).
32. Grundfest, H., Reuben, J. P., and Rickles, W. H., Jr. The electrophysiology and pharmacology of lobster neuromuscular synapses. *J. Gen. Physiol.*, *42:* 1301-1323 (1959).
33. Hagiwara, S., Kusano, K., and Saito, N. Membrane changes in crayfish stretch receptor neuron during inhibition and under action of gamma-aminobutyric acid. *J. Neurophysiol.*, *23:* 505-515 (1960).

34. Hagiwara, S., and Saito, N. Voltage-current relations in nerve cell membrane of *Onchidium verruculatum*. *J. Physiol.*, (Lond.), *148:* 161-179 (1959).

35. Hodgkin, A. L. The Croonian Lecture: Ionic movements and electrical activity in giant nerve fibres. *Proc. Roy. Soc. Lond. (B)*, *148:* 1-37 (1957).

36. Hodgkin, A. L., and Horowicz, P. Movements of Na and K in single muscle fibres. *J. Physiol. (Lond.)*, *145:* 405-432 (1959).

37. Hodgkin, A. L., and Huxley, A. F. A quantitative description of membrane current and its applications to conduction and excitation in nerve. *J. Physiol.* (Lond.), *117:* 500-544 (1952).

38. Hodgkin, A. L., and Katz, B. The effect of sodium ions on the electrical activity of the giant axon of the squid. *J. Physiol.* (Lond.), *108:* 37-77 (1949).

39. Hutter, O. Ionic movements during vagus inhibition of the heart. In, *Nervous Inhibition* (E. Florey, Ed.), Pergamon Press, London, 1961.

40. Keynes, R. D., Bennett, M. V. L., and Grundfest, H. Studies on morphology and electrophysiology of electric organs. II. Electrophysiology of electric organ of *Malapterurus electricus*. In, *Bioelectrogenesis* (C. Chagas and A. Paes de Carvalho, Eds.), Elsevier, Amsterdam, 1961.

41. Koketsu, K. A concept of the mechanism of active depolarization. In, *Biophysics of Physiological and Pharmacological Actions* (A. M. Shanes, Ed.), American Association for the Advancement of Science, Washington, D. C., 1961.

42. Kuffler, S. W., and Vaughan-Williams, E. M. Properties of the "slow" skeletal muscle fibres of the frog. *J. Physiol.* (Lond.), *121:* 318-340 (1953).

43. Lorente de Nó, R. *A Study of Nerve Physiology.* The Rockefeller Institute for Medical Research, Studies Vols. 131 and 132, 1947.

44. Lüttgau, H. C. Das Kalium-Transportsystem am Ranvier-Knoten isolierter markhaltiger Nervenfasern. *Pflugers Archiv.*, *271:* 613-633 (1960).

45. Noble, D. Cardiac action and pacemaker potentials based on the Hodgkin-Huxley equations. *Nature, 188:* 495-497 (1960).

46. Reuben, J. P., Werman, R., and Grundfest, H. The ionic mechanisms of hyperpolarizing responses in lobster muscle fibers. *J. Gen. Physiol.*, *45:* 243-265. (1961).

47. Roche, M. (Ed.). Physiology of the cell membrane. *J. Gen. Physiol.*, *43:* Suppl. 1 (1960).

48. Shanes, A. M. Electrochemical aspects of physiological and pharmacological actions in excitable cells. *Pharmacol. Revs.*, *10:* 59-273 (1958).

49. Spyropoulos, C. S., and Tasaki, I. Nerve excitation and synaptic transmission. *Ann. Rev. Physiol.*, *22:* 407-432 (1960).

50. Tasaki, I. Demonstration of two stable states of the nerve membrane in potassium-rich media. *J. Physiol.* (Lond.), *148:* 306-331 (1959).

51. Tasaki, I. Conduction of the nerve impulse. In, *Handbook of Physiology, Section 1, Neurophysiology I* (J. Field, Ed.), American Physiological Society, Washington, D. C., 1959.

52. Tasaki, I., and Hagiwara, S. Demonstration of two stable potential states in the squid giant axon under tetraethylammonium chloride. *J. Gen. Physiol.*, *40:* 858-885 (1957).

53. Teorell, T. Electrokinetic membrane processes in relation to properties of excitable tissues. *J. Gen. Physiol.*, *42:* 831-863 (1959).

54. Weidmann, S. *Electrophysiologie der Herzmuskelfaser.* Hans Huber, Bern, 1956.

55. Werman, R., and Grundfest, H. Graded and all-or-none electrogenesis in arthropod muscle. II. The effect of alkali-earth and onium ions on lobster muscle fibers. *J. Gen. Physiol.*, *44:* 997-1027 (1961).

56. Werman, R., McCann, F. V., and Grundfest, H. Graded and all-or-none electrogenesis in arthropod muscle. I. The effects of alkali-earth cations on the neuromuscular system of *Romalea microptera. J. Gen. Physiol.*, *44:* 979-995 (1961).

57. Wolstenholme, G. E. W., and O'Connor, C. M. (Eds.) *Regulation of the Inorganic Ion Content of Cells* (Ciba Foundation Study Group No. 5). Little, Brown and Co., Boston, 1960.

Discussion

ICHIJI TASAKI

Dr. Grundfest's view on the ionic basis of electrogenesis in the nerve and muscle membrane is based on his thorough and extensive survey of the behavior of various excitable tissues. His view is well known in the field of neurophysiology; some part of it is shared by many investigators in the field. There is no doubt in our minds that the distribution and the movements of various ions *across* the membrane are important factors in the production of the resting and action potentials in cellular membranes.

In Dr. Grundfest's presentation the chemical and structural aspects of the membrane play only a subsidiary role. The structure of the membrane is brought into consideration simply as variable diffusion-barriers for various ions. To his mind, the membrane represents a dielectric condenser, battery and resistor. In a sense, this view is a refinement of Hodgkin and Huxley's electrical circuit model of the nerve membrane.

A minority of investigators, whose views I share, emphasizes the importance of the structure and chemistry of the nerve membrane itself. It is generally believed that the thickness of the nerve membrane is 50 to 100 Å. Across such a structure, ions cannot jump in one step. For sodium-ion to be able to cross the membrane, its concentration in the membrane has to be finite. It is well known that (ionic conductance) = (ionic mobility) $\times$ (ion concentration).

When the electric conductance of the nerve membrane rises during excitation by a factor of 10 to 400, probably both the concentration and the mobility of various ions in the membrane rise above the resting levels for a short period of time.

It is obvious that ions in the membrane cannot violate the condition of electrical neutrality. To permit sodium-ions to stay in the membrane, mobile or fixed "electrically negative sites" must exist in the nerve membrane.

100

(There is some evidence, to be related later, that they are fixed sites.) These negative sites are in all probability carboxyl, phosphoric or other acid radicals. This leads us to the "charged membrane theory," promulgated for many years by Michaelis, Teorell, Meyer and Sievers, and others but on the whole ignored by investigators in this field.

If we accept the existence of fixed charges in the nerve membrane, several inferences can be made, some of which can be tested by experiment.

1. The membrane potential is given by the sum of the potential drops across the two interfaces and the diffusion potential in the membrane. In the excited state (and to a lesser extent in the resting state) of the membrane the potential drop across the stagnant layer outside the membrane may also make a significant contribution.

2. As emphasized originally by Planck and more recently experimentally by Teorell, the concentration profiles for individual ions in the membrane play decisive roles in determining the membrane potential, membrane current, membrane permeability, stability, etc.

3. There exists competition and interaction between ions in the membrane.

As we know, the potential difference across a glass membrane (used for pH measurements) is determined at the interfaces between the aqueous and glass phases. The permeability of ions through the glass proper has no effect upon the overall potential. In cation-exchange membranes with high fixed charge, the potential field within the membrane is rather small and the potential drops are localized mainly at the interfaces (Donnan effect).

Recently, Spyropoulos, Teorell and myself made an extensive survey of the membrane permeability by the use of radioactive tracers. Part of this investigation is an extension of the work done by Hodgkin, Keynes and others. We found that the nerve membrane is highly perm-selective: various cations can much more readily go through the membrane than anions. Such perm-selectivity becomes very high during the excited state of the membrane. This suggests that the nerve membrane has a property of a cation-exchanger. More recently, Teorell and Spyropoulos obtained independent evidence indicating the existence of a fixed charge in the squid axon membrane. We cannot therefore ignore the possibility that the resting and action potentials are determined by Donnan effects at interfaces rather than by ionic permeabilities within the substance of the membrane.

A consideration of concentration profiles within the membrane leads us to the following possibility as to the nature of ionic current: the species of ion carrying the major portion of the electric charge across the membrane may vary from one layer to another within the membrane. An inward current may be carried at the outer surface of the membrane mainly by sodium (because it is the major cation in the medium, and anions do not seem to be highly permeable). Near the inner surface of the membrane, potassium ions may carry the major portion of the charge.

The proposed negative sites in the membrane can accept various kinds of cations with different degrees of preference. From this it follows that ions within the membrane are mutually exclusive: if under a certain condition sodium concentration in the membrane rises, the concentrations of other ions tend to fall (if there is no net increase in the fixed charge). Therefore, the ionic conductances in such a membrane cannot vary independently. A change in the conductance for one ion species in general brings about changes in the conductances for other ions.

A long time ago, Alexander, Aborg, and Teorell investigated competition between calcium ions and univalent ions in the membrane made of cephaline. Coleman, Gregor and others investigated similar competition in cation-exchange membranes. Recently, we have shown that such competition can explain the changes in the movement of radioactive sodium or potassium caused by a change in the calcium concentration in the medium. Spyropoulos has shown further that such a competition can explain some aspects of initiation and abolition of action potentials in the frog single node preparation.

In the modern theory of thermodynamics of irreversible processes, movement of one kind of particle across the membrane is considered to affect the movement or distribution of other mobile particles in the membrane. An interaction between the movement of "metabolites" and ions can in principle explain the so-called ionic pumps and active transports. The possibility of the existence of chemical reactions within the membrane can be properly incorporated in such a theoretical consideration. In such a treatment, it is not proper to make a sharp distinction between "active" and "passive" transport processes; it simply shows that the equations used in previous physiological considerations are insufficient or incorrect.

In conclusion, the ionic theory which is now widely accepted can have a better and more concrete foundation if the chemistry and structure of the membrane itself are taken into consideration.